Zaner-Bloser
SPELLING CONNECTIONS

J. Richard Gentry, Ph.D.

1

Series Author
J. Richard Gentry, Ph.D.

Art Buyer: Signature Design Group

Photography: George C. Anderson: cover; pages 1, 3, 6, 177

Illustrations: Heidi Chang, Lauren Cryan, Richard Kolding, Vickie Learner, Diana Magnuson, Miriam Sagasti, N. Jo Tufts

ISBN: 0-7367-0037-4

Copyright © 2000 Zaner-Bloser, Inc.

Zaner-Bloser, Inc., P.O. Box 16764, Columbus, Ohio 43216-6764 (1-800-421-3018)

Printed in the United States of America   01 02 03 QP 5 4

Contents

Name _____

Identifying Initial Sounds

Say the name of this picture:  .

Circle the pictures that start with the same sound.

School/Home
Help your child name other words that start like **tent**.

Identifying Initial Sounds   7

Phonemic Awareness

Recognizing Rhyme

Say the name of this picture:  .

Say the name of each picture. Circle the pictures that rhyme with **cat**.

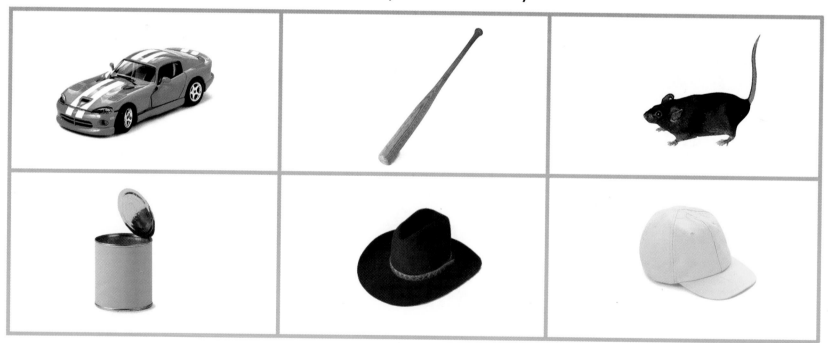

 School/Home
Help your child name other words that rhyme with **cat**.

Name _____

Counting Sounds in Words

Say the name of this picture: 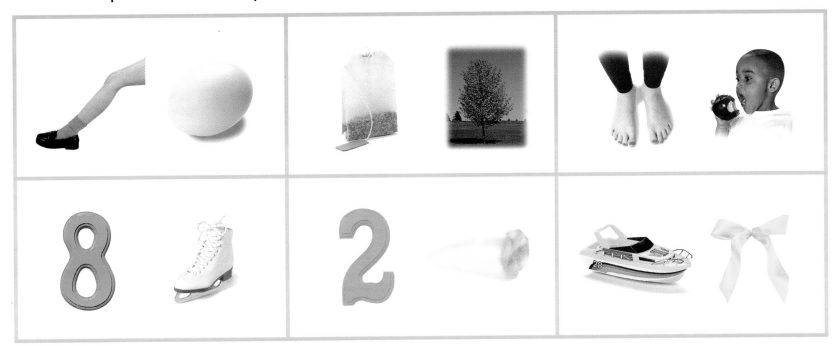. **Bee** has two sounds.

Say the first sound in **bee**: **b**. Say the second sound in **bee**: **e**.

Say the name of this picture: . **Bean** has three sounds.

Circle the picture in each pair with two sounds.

School/Home
Make a list of simple words. Take turns with your child as you say
the sounds and guess the number of sounds in each word.

Counting Sounds in Words

Say:  **bag**. Say the first sound in **bag**: **b**. Say the second sound in **bag**: **a**. Say the third sound in **bag**: **g**. **Bag** has three sounds. Say the name of each picture. Draw an **X** on the pictures whose names have three sounds.

School/Home
Play a game with your child. Start saying words with only two or three sounds. Take turns guessing the number of sounds in each other's words.

Name _____

Sounds and Letters

Bb

● Say the name of each picture.
Draw an **X** through the pictures that begin with **b** like **ball**.

■ Write **b** to complete each spelling.

_____ ee   ox   us

▲ Trace. Practice.

B B

b b

School/Home
This page provides practice in reviewing the sound of initial **Bb**.
Help your child name the pictures and practice writing the letter.

C c

● Say the name of each picture.
Circle the pictures that begin with **c** like  **cat**.

■ Write **c** to complete each spelling.

up   ub   ar

▲ Trace. Practice.

C C

c c

School/Home
This page provides practice in reviewing the sound of initial **Cc**.
Help your child name the pictures and practice writing the letter.

Name _____

Sounds and Letters

● Say the name of each picture.
Circle the pictures that begin with **d** like **desk**.

■ Write **d** to complete each spelling.

_____ eer   _____ ish   _____ og

▲ Trace. Practice.

School/Home
This page provides practice in reviewing the sound of initial **Dd**.
Help your child name the pictures and practice writing the letter.

Ff

● Look at each picture and say its name.
Draw an **X** through the pictures that begin with **f** like  **fish**.

 | 5 |  |

■ Write **f** to complete each spelling.

_____ ork   _____ ive   _____ ox

▲ Trace. Practice.

F F

f f

 School/Home
This page provides practice in reviewing the sound of initial **Ff**.
Help your child name the pictures and practice writing the letter.

Name _____

Gg

● Say the name of each picture.
Circle the pictures that begin with **g** like **gate**.

■ Write **g** to complete each spelling.

__irl   __oat   __um

▲ Trace. Practice.

 G   G

 g   g

  School/Home
This page provides practice in reviewing the sound of initial **Gg**.
Help your child name the pictures and practice writing the letter.

Hh

● Say the name of each picture.
Color the pictures that begin with **h** like **heart**.

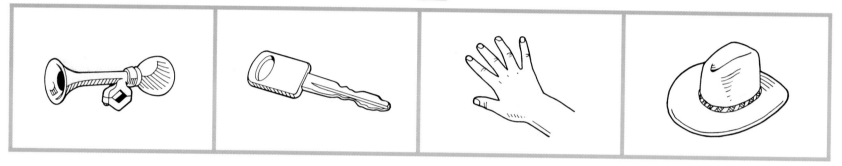

■ Write **h** to complete each spelling.

___orn   ___and   ___at

▲ Trace. Practice.

School/Home
This page provides practice in reviewing the sound of initial **Hh**.
Help your child name the pictures and practice writing the letter.

Name _____

● Say the name of each picture.
Draw an **X** through the pictures that begin with **j** like **jack-o'-lantern**.

■ Write **j** to complete each spelling.

_____ar   _____et   _____eep

▲ Trace. Practice.

 School/Home
This page provides practice in reviewing the sound of initial **Jj**.
Help your child name the pictures and practice writing the letter.

17

 **Kk**

Sounds and Letters

● Say the name of each picture.
  Draw a line under the pictures that begin with **k** like **kitten**.

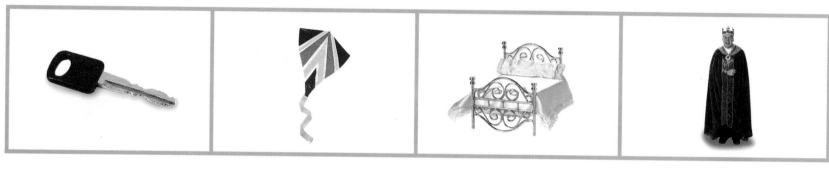

■ Write **k** to complete each spelling.

_____ey   _____ite   _____ing

▲ Trace. Practice.

K K

k k

School/Home
This page provides practice in reviewing the sound of initial **Kk**.
Help your child name the pictures and practice writing the letter.

Sounds and Letters

LI

● Look at each picture and say its name.
  Draw an **X** through the pictures that begin with **l** like **lion**.

■ Write **l** to complete each spelling.

_____eaf   _____ake   _____ips

▲ Trace. Practice.

School/Home
This page provides practice in reviewing the sound of initial **Ll**.
Help your child name the pictures and practice writing the letter.

19

Mm

● Look at each picture and say its name.
Circle the pictures that begin with **m** like **men**.

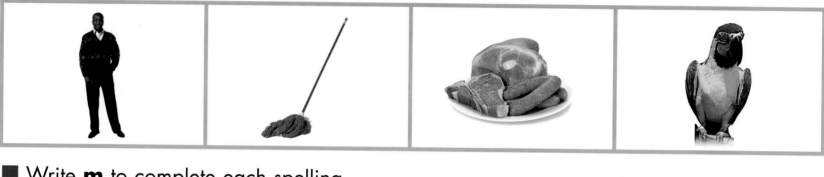

■ Write **m** to complete each spelling.

an op eat

▲ Trace. Practice.

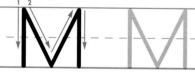

School/Home
This page provides practice in reviewing the sound of initial **Mm**.
Help your child name the pictures and practice writing the letter.

Name _____

Sounds **and** Letters

● Look at each picture and say the name.
Draw a line under the pictures that begin with **n** like **9** **nine**.

■ Write **n** to complete each spelling.

___ut   ___est   ___ose

▲ Trace. Practice.

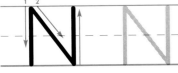

School/Home
This page provides practice in reviewing the sound of initial **Nn**.
Help your child name the pictures and practice writing the letter.

21

Pp

● Say the name of each picture.
Draw an **X** over the pictures that begin with **p** like  **pot**.

■ Write **p** to complete each spelling.

___en ___aw ___ie

▲ Trace. Practice.

P P P

p p p

 **School/Home**
This page provides practice in reviewing the sound of initial **Pp**.
Help your child name the pictures and practice writing the letter.

Name _____

Sounds and **Letters**

Qq

● Say the name of each picture.
Draw a box around the pictures that begin with **q** like  **quarter**.

■ Write **q** to complete each spelling.

_____ueen   _____uack   _____uilt

▲ Trace. Practice.

School/Home
This page provides practice in reviewing the sound of initial **Qq**.
Help your child name the pictures and practice writing the letter.

Rr

● Look at each picture and say its name.
Color the pictures that begin with **r** like **ring**.

■ Write **r** to complete each spelling.

___ope   ___ake   ___ock

▲ Trace. Practice.

R R

r r

School/Home
This page provides practice in reviewing the sound of initial **Rr**.
Help your child name the pictures and practice writing the letter.

Name _____

Ss

● Look at each picture and say its name.
Draw a line under the pictures that begin with **s** like **saddle**.

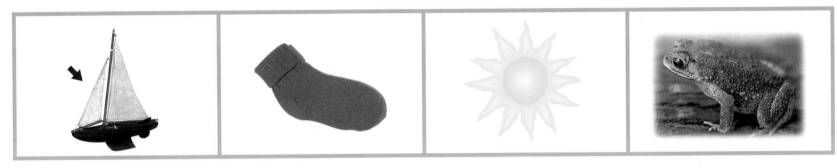

■ Write **s** to complete each spelling.

___ail   ___ock   ___un

▲ Trace. Practice.

S S

s s

 School/Home
This page provides practice in reviewing the sound of initial **Ss**.
Help your child name the pictures and practice writing the letter.

25

Tt

● Listen as you say the name of each picture.
Circle the pictures that begin with **t** like ➜ **tail**.

■ Write **t** to complete each spelling.

___op   ___en   ___oys

▲ Trace. Practice.

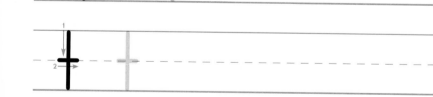

School/Home
This page provides practice in reviewing the sound of initial **Tt**.
Help your child name the pictures and practice writing the letter.

Name _____

● Say the name of each picture.
Draw an **X** over the pictures that begin with **v** like **vest**.

■ Write **v** to complete each spelling.

an   ase   et

▲ Trace. Practice.

 V

v

 School/Home
This page provides practice in reviewing the sound of initial **Vv**.
Help your child name the pictures and practice writing the letter.

27

Ww

● Say the name of each picture.
Draw a box around the pictures that begin with **w** like **watch**.

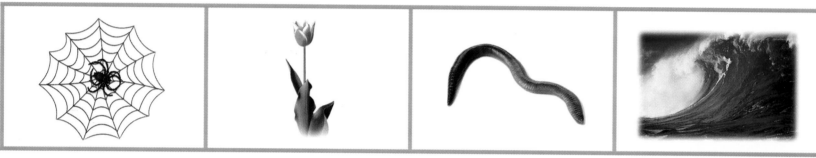

■ Write **w** to complete each spelling.

eb   orm   ave

▲ Trace. Practice.

School/Home
This page provides practice in reviewing the sound of initial **Ww**.
Help your child name the pictures and practice writing the letter.

Sounds *and* **Letters**

● Say the name of each picture.
Color the pictures that end with **x** like **box**.

■ Write **x** to complete each spelling.

fo   a   o

▲ Trace. Practice.

School/Home
This page provides practice in reviewing the sound of final **Xx**.
Help your child name the pictures and practice writing the letter.

Yy

Sounds and Letters

● Look at each picture and say its name.
Draw an **X** through the pictures that begin with **y** like  **yellow**.

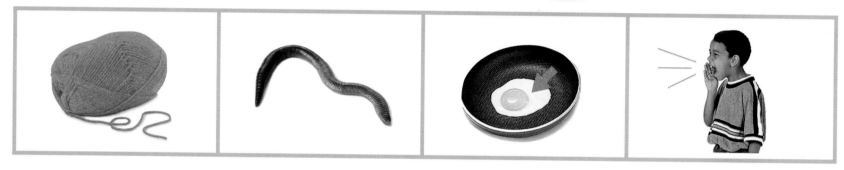

■ Write **y** to complete each spelling.

arn

olk

ell

▲ Trace. Practice.

Y Y

y y

30

School/Home
This page provides practice in reviewing the sound of initial **Yy**.
Help your child name the pictures and practice writing the letter.

Name _____

Sounds and Letters

Zz

● Look at each picture and say its name.
Draw a box around the pictures that begin with **z** like **zipper**.

■ Write **z** to complete each spelling.

ebra   oo   ero

▲ Trace. Practice.

Z z

Z z

School/Home
This page provides practice in reviewing the sound of initial **Zz**.
Help your child name the pictures and practice writing the letter.

Aa

● Look at each picture and say its name.
Draw an **X** through the pictures that begin with **a** like **apple**.

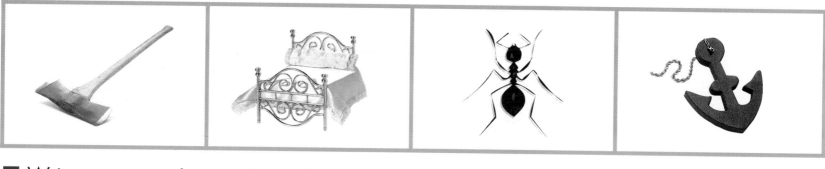

■ Write **a** to complete each spelling.

x   nt   nchor

▲ Trace. Practice.

School/Home
This page provides practice in reviewing the sound of initial **Aa**.
Help your child name the pictures and practice writing the letter.

Sounds and Letters

Ee

● Look at each picture and say its name.
Circle the pictures that begin with **e** like **EXIT** **exit**.

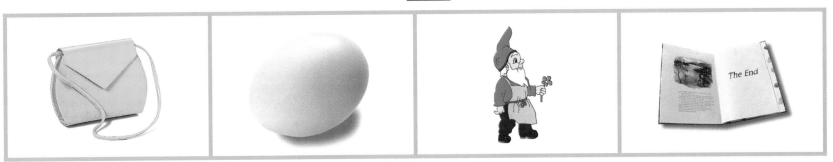

■ Write **e** to complete each spelling.

gg   lf   nd

▲ Trace. Practice.

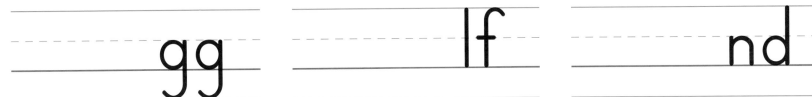

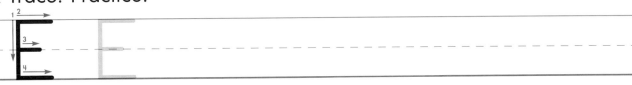

School/Home
This page provides practice in reviewing the sound of initial **Ee**.
Help your child name the pictures and practice writing the letter.

33

I i

● Say the name of each picture.
  Color the pictures that begin with **i** like **igloo**.

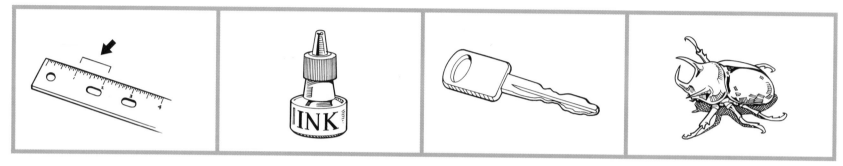

■ Write **i** to complete each spelling.

nch   nk   nsect

▲ Trace. Practice.

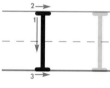

School/Home
This page provides practice in reviewing the sound of initial **Ii**.
Help your child name the pictures and practice writing the letter.

Name _____

● Say the name of each picture.
Circle the pictures that begin with **o** like **ostrich**.

■ Write **o** to complete each spelling.

live   x   ff

▲ Trace. Practice.

 **School/Home**
This page provides practice in reviewing the sound of initial **Oo**.
Help your child name the pictures and practice writing the letter.

Uu

● Say the name of each picture.
  Color the pictures that begin with **u** like **umbrella**.

■ Write **u** to complete each spelling.

____ p   ____ nder   ____ mpire

▲ Trace. Practice.

School/Home
This page provides practice in reviewing the sound of initial **Uu**.
Help your child name the pictures and practice writing the letter.

Spelling and Thinking

1. an
2. can
3. man
4. ran
5. had
6. dad

A. Write the spelling words that end with **an**.

1. _____

2. _____

3. _____

4. _____

B. Write the spelling words that end with **ad**.

5. _____

6. _____

C. Use your pencil to track the letters in a-b-c order. The first two are tracked for you.

d f (a) g (b) w r c l s e d v e f
a o b g t h d q u i n j h k l
m z c n d o q i x p d s q r w
s g t o m r a u b s v w h q x
l y v z u t

School/Home
This unit targets the **short a** sound. Ask your child to name other words that rhyme with **an**.

Short a 37

Spelling and Phonics

an
can
man
ran
had
dad

A. Draw a line to match each spelling word with the picture name that begins with the same sound.

1. an   2. dad   3. had   4. man   5. ran   6. can

B. Write the word that rhymes with the underlined word and completes the meaning.

7. A girl was in the race: <u>Jan</u> _____

8. Someone who likes a team: <u>fan</u> _____

9. A happy father: <u>glad</u> _____

Name _____

Spelling and Reading

Write the missing spelling words.

an	**can**	**dad**

1. My _____ is a teacher.

2. I have _____ apple.

3. You _____ paint with me.

had	**man**	**ran**

4. We _____ to your house.

5. A _____ is on the swing.

6. The worm _____ a hat.

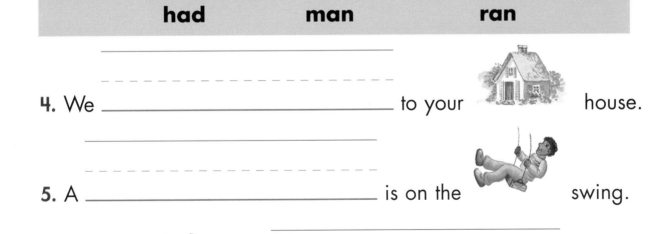

an
can
man
ran
had
dad

Spelling and Writing

Write a story about this picture.

More Words for Writing ▶ ant   lap   tag   pants

Write the word that rhymes with the picture name.

1. The ants have on _____

_____ .

_____

2. The  cap is on her _____

_____ .

_____

3. Grant sat on an _____

_____ .

_____

4. The flag can wave its _____

_____ .

_____

Name _____

Spelling and Thinking

1. am
2. at
3. cat
4. hat
5. has
6. and

A. Write the spelling words that begin like **apple**.

1. _____

2. _____

3. _____

B. Write the spelling words that have **short a** in the middle, like **bat**.

4. _____

5. _____

6. _____

School/Home
This unit targets the **short a** sound. Ask your child to read the words on the spelling list.

Short a **41**

am
at
cat
hat
has
and

A. Write the two words that begin with **h**.
Circle the letters that are the same.

1. _____

2. _____

B. Write the words that rhyme with the picture names.

3. _____

5. _____

4. _____

6. _____

7. _____

Name _____

Spelling **and** Reading

am
at
cat
hat
has
and

Write the correct word in each sentence.

has   **cat**

1. The _____ ran up a tree.

2. The man _____ a hammer.

am   **and**

3. I _____ happy.

4. I can run _____ jump.

at   **hat**

5. The monkey had on a tan _____.

6. Jan is _____ school.

Spelling and Writing

Cat-astrophe

Cat is fat.
When he sat
On my hat,
Hat went splat.
That was that!

— Kevin O'Hara

Write other words that rhyme with **cat**. Use some of these words to make a rhyme of your own. Draw a picture to go with your rhyme.

More Words for Writing ▶ **bag   pan   mat   lamp**

Write the word that goes with the others.

1. pot   skillet
_____

2. pail   box
_____

3. candle   flashlight
_____

4. rug   tiles
_____

Spelling and **Thinking**

1. let
2. get
3. net
4. pet
5. pen
6. men

A. Write the spelling words that end with **et**.

1. _____
2. _____

3. _____
4. _____

B. Write the spelling words that end with **en**.

5. _____
6. _____

School/Home
This unit teaches **short e**. Ask your child to find the rhyming words on the spelling list.

Spelling and Phonics

let
get
net
pet
pen
men

A. Four spelling words rhyme. Write the words.
Circle the letters that are the same.

1. _____

2. _____

3. _____

4. _____

B. Write the word that tells about each picture.

5. ten ___?___

6. hen ___?___

7. wet ___?___

8. get ___?___

Name _____

Spelling and Reading

Write the missing spelling words.

let
get
net
pet
pen
men

men	pen

_____

1. Sam has a red _____.

_____

2. The _____ ran on the sand.

let	pet	get	net

_____

3. The _____ has a hole in it.

_____

4. Pam can _____ a fan.

_____

5. Ben has a _____.

_____

6. Dan _____ the cat in.

Short e 47

Spelling *and* Writing

What if a hen's egg would not hatch? What could be wrong with the egg? Will anything ever come out of it? Write what you think will happen.

More Words for Writing ▶ **hen   den   wet   fed**

Complete the missing words.

Jan _f_____ the _w_____ _h_____ in the _d_____ .

Write a sentence using **hen** and **wet**.
Write a sentence using **den** and **fed**.

Spelling and Thinking

1. jet
2. set
3. met
4. bed
5. yes
6. leg

A. Write the spelling words that end with **et**.

1. _____

2. _____

3. _____

B. Answer each riddle.

4. This word means
the opposite of "no." _____

_____

5. Your foot is at the
end of it. _____

_____

6. You sleep on it. _____

_____

School/Home
This unit teaches **short e**. Ask your child to read the words on the spelling list aloud.

Short e 49

Spelling and Phonics

jet
set
met
bed
yes
leg

A. Use the clues to find the word. Write each word.

1. Begins like  .

Rhymes with .

_____

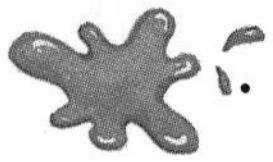

2. Begins like  .

Rhymes with .

_____

3. Begins like .

Rhymes with .

_____

B. Write the three words that rhyme.
Circle the letters that are the same.

4. _____

5. _____

6. _____

Name _____

Write the words.

1.–2. Is the leg on the bed bad?

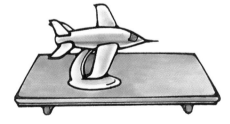

_____   _____

The _____ on the _____ is bad.

_____   _____

3.–4. Have you met Meg?

_____   _____

_____ , I have _____ Meg.

_____   _____

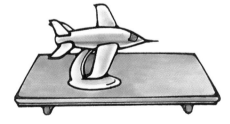

5.–6. Did you set your jet on the shelf?

_____   _____

I _____ my _____ on the shelf.

_____   _____

Short e 51

jet
set
met
bed
yes
leg

Spelling and Writing

Yes, a young yellow yak yelled, "Yippee!"

Use the rest of the spelling words to make tongue twisters of your own.

- The jolly jet …
- Mice met …
- Sue set …
- Bill's bed …

YIPPEE

More Words for Writing ▶ **led   vest   mend   mess**

Write the words to complete the meaning.

I.–2. Did the robin _____ her old _____ ?

3.–4. Jan _____ Tim out of the _____ .

Review Unit 1: Short a

A. Write the spelling word that has two letters.

I. _____

B. Add a letter to **ad** to make two new words.

h d

2. _____   3. _____

Add a letter to **an** to make three new words.

c m r

4. _____   5. _____

6. _____

1. an

2. can

3. man

4. ran

5. had

6. dad

School/Home
This unit reviews **short a** and **short e**. Ask your child to read the spelling list on each page aloud.

Review 53

1. am
2. at
3. cat
4. hat
5. has
6. and

A. Write the spelling words that end with **at**.

1. _____ 2. _____

3. _____

B. Write a spelling word to fill each blank.

4. Jack _____ Jill went up the hill.

5. I _____ so smart.

6. Our cat _____ three kittens.

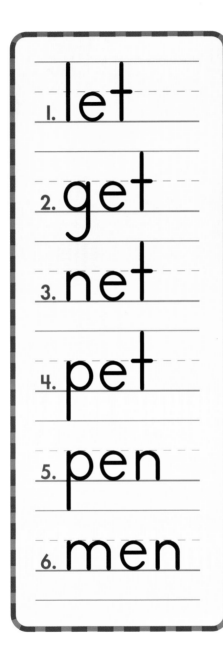

1. let
2. get
3. net
4. pet
5. pen
6. men

A. 1. Write the spelling word that means .

2. Change one letter to make a word that means .

3. Change one letter to make a word that means .

4. Change one letter to make a word that means .

B. Write the spelling word to fill in each blank.

5. Please _____ the cat out.

6. Did you _____ a gift?

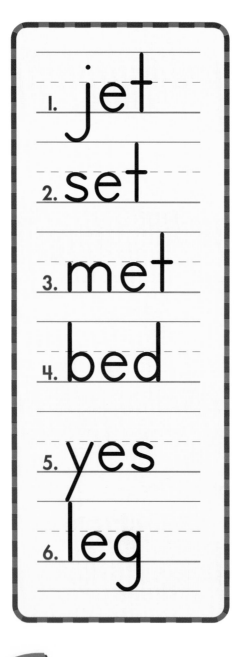

1. jet
2. set
3. met
4. bed
5. yes
6. leg

A. Write the spelling word to fill in each blank.

1. You sit in a chair. You sleep on a __?__ .

2. Your hand is on your arm.

   Your foot is on your __?__ .

3. **Off** is opposite of **on**. **No** is opposite of __?__ .

1. _____   2. _____

3. _____

B. Write the words that rhyme with **get**.

4. _____   5. _____

6. _____

Name _____

Spelling and Thinking

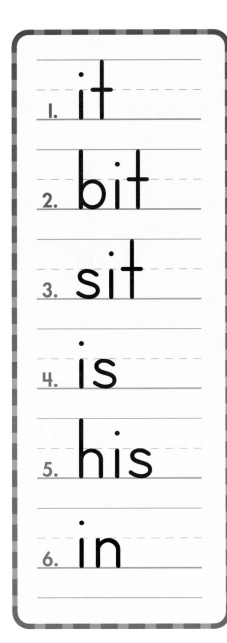

1. it
2. bit
3. sit
4. is
5. his
6. in

A. Write the spelling words that end with **is**.

1. _____ 2. _____

B. Write the spelling words that end with **it**.

3. _____ 4. _____

5. _____

C. Write the spelling word that ends with **n**.

6. _____

School/Home
This unit teaches **short i**. Ask your child to name words that rhyme with **bit**.

A. Write the spelling words with two sounds.

1. _____

2. _____

3. _____

it
bit
sit
is
his
in

B. Use the letters in the blocks to make words. Write the words.

4. **b** + **it** = _____

5. **s** + **it** = _____

6. **h** + **is** = _____

Name _____

Write the letters in the shapes. Then write each sentence.

1. The big hat ☐☐ ☐☐☐ .

2. Sam ☐☐☐ ☐☐ .

3. Dad can ☐☐☐ ☐☐ the sand.

it
bit
sit
is
his
in

1. _____

2. _____

3. _____

Short i 59

The Dog and His Bone

What is the lesson of this fable? Write your own story about someone who wanted something.

More Words for Writing ▶ sip lid tip wig

Write the missing words.

1. I can __?__ from the glass.

2. The __?__ fits the pan.

3. Nan has a __?__ .

4. The __?__ of the pen is bad.

Spelling and Thinking

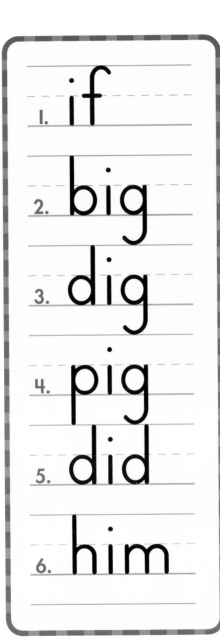

1. if
2. big
3. dig
4. pig
5. did
6. him

A. Write the spelling words that end in **ig**.

1. _____

2. _____

3. _____

B. Write the spelling word with two letters.

4. _____

C. Write the word that is the same backward and forward.

5. _____

D. Write the word that goes with **her**.

6. _____

School/Home
This unit targets the **short i** sound. Help your child read the words on the spelling list aloud.

Spelling *and* Phonics

Write the word that rhymes with the underlined word and goes with the picture.

1. Ben has a <u>dig</u>.

_____

- - - - - - - - - - - -

_____

2. Dad's hand is <u>pig</u>.

_____

- - - - - - - - - - - -

_____

3. I <u>hid</u> get a pet.

_____

- - - - - - - - - - - -

_____

4. The cat ran to <u>dim</u>.

_____

- - - - - - - - - - - -

_____

5. The men will <u>big</u> a hole.

_____

- - - - - - - - - - - -

_____

6. Get the hat <u>stiff</u> you can.

_____

- - - - - - - - - - - -

_____

if

big

dig

pig

did

him

Name _____

Spelling and Reading

Write each spelling word once to complete the story.

Once there was a pink __1.__ named Squeak.
He would dig in his pen. He would dig in the yard.
He loved to __2.__ .

Squeak saw a garden full of vegetables.
Squeak said, "I want to eat those vegetables.
Maybe __3.__ I dig a __4.__ hole I will get to the
garden." And he __5.__ ! Squeak ate and ate.

"Get __6.__ !" shouted the farmer. "Get him out of my garden!"

Squeak ran to his pen and hid. He never tried to dig out of the
pen again!

| if |
| big |
| dig |
| pig |
| did |
| him |

1. _____

2. _____

3. _____

4. _____

5. _____

6. _____

Spelling and Writing

Give the story of the "Three Little Pigs" a different ending.

"Little Pig, Little Pig, let me come in!"
"No! Not by the hair on my chinny-chin-chin!"
Then the wolf …

More Words for Writing ▶ bib   rip   pin   zip

Write a word to finish each rhyme.

1. For first place you will win
   A shiny, purple

_____

_____ .

2. My old jacket has a rip
   And now it will no longer

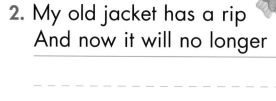

_____

_____ .

3. The little baby in her crib
   Wears a brand-new, fluffy

_____

_____ .

4. With your scissors you can snip.
   With your fingers you can

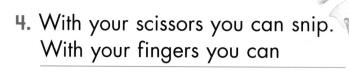

_____

_____ .

Name _____

Spelling and Thinking

Unit **8**

Short o

1. not
2. hot
3. pot
4. got
5. box
6. fox

Write the letters in a-b-c order. Write the spelling word that begins with each letter.

f b g

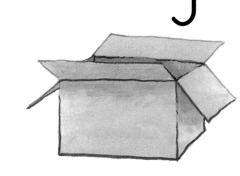

1. _____ _____
2. _____ _____
3. _____ _____

h p n

1. _____ _____
2. _____ _____
3. _____ _____

School/Home
This unit is about **short o**. Ask your child to name other words that rhyme with **hot**.

Short o 65

Spelling and Phonics

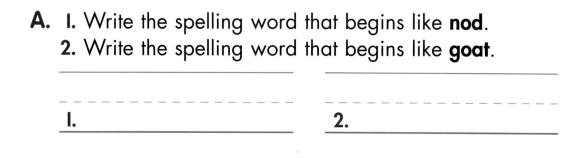

A. 1. Write the spelling word that begins like **nod**.
2. Write the spelling word that begins like **goat**.

1. _____

2. _____

B. Write the spelling word that names each picture.
Circle the letters that are the same in each word.

3. _____

4. _____

5. _____

6. _____

not
hot
pot
got
box
fox

Name _____

Write the missing spelling words to build a story.

The Hot Fox

1. This is the _____ _____ .

2. The hot fox _____ a rock.

3. The hot fox got the rock in a _____ .

4. The hot fox got the rock in a pot in a _____ .

5. The hot fox who got the rock in a pot in a box could _____ jog.

| not |
| hot |
| pot |
| got |
| box |
| fox |

Spelling *and* Writing

Do you think the fox can trick the crow?
What will the fox say to the crow?
Why does the fox want to trick the crow?
Tell what will happen next.

More Words for Writing ▶ **ox   cod   jog   trot**

Write the missing words.

1. The cod has fins. The _____ has horns.

2. A bird can fly. A _____ can swim.

3. Fish swim. Horses _____ . People _____ .

Spelling and Thinking

Count and hop to find words.

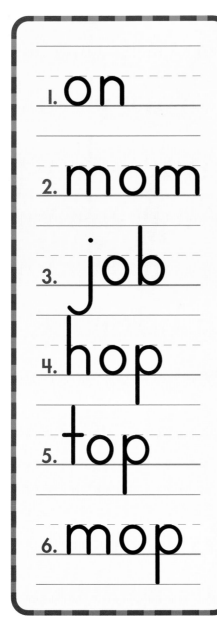

1. on
2. mom
3. job
4. hop
5. top
6. mop

b	h	j	m	n	o	p	t

→ 6
← 1   1. _____

→ 4
→ 2   3. _____
→ 1

→ 3
→ 3   5. _____
← 5

→ 8
← 2   2. _____
→ 1

→ 4
→ 2   4. _____
← 2

→ 2
→ 4   6. _____
→ 1

School/Home
This unit teaches **short o**. Help your child read the words in the spelling list aloud.

Short o   69

Spelling and Phonics

on
mom
job
hop
top
mop

Write the word that rhymes with the underlined word.

_____

1. Tom has a pin for his _____ .

_____

2. Drop the lid on _____ .

_____

3. I had to stop and _____ the floor.

_____

4. Bob has a big _____ .

_____

5. Jon was _____ a mat.

_____

6. The balloon will pop when I _____ .

Name _____

Spelling and Reading

Look at the picture. Write the spelling word to complete the sentence.

1. I will help _____ .

2. Dad is at his _____ .

3. _____ has a big hat.

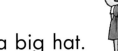

4. The hen is _____ a box.

5. The bug will _____ to the red dot.

6. Ron will get to the _____ .

on

mom

job

hop

top

mop

Spelling and Writing

What would happen if the hare in "The Tortoise and the Hare" raced a different animal? Write about it. Use this as the first line of your story.

One day a hare met a …

More Words for Writing ▸ hog   rod   jot   body

Write the missing words.

1. Another name for a pig is __?__ .

2. A long pole is a __?__ .

3. Each person's __?__ is different.

4. To write something quickly is to __?__ it down.

Spelling List

1. it
2. bit
3. sit
4. is
5. his
6. in

Write two spelling words to finish each sentence.

1.–2. This book _____ _____ _____ .

3.–4. I will _____ _____ _____ this chair.

5.–6. Ow! _____ _____ _____ me!

School/Home
This unit reviews the **short i** and **short o**. Ask your child to read the spelling list on each page aloud.

1. if
2. big
3. dig
4. pig
5. did
6. him

A. Follow the directions to make new words.

1. Write the spelling word that means "not small."

_____

2. Change one letter to make [pig].

_____

3. Change one letter to make [dig].

_____

4. Change one letter to make a word that is the same backward and forward.

_____

B. Write a word in each blank.

_____

5. We play inside _____ it rains.

_____

6. Did you see _____ ?

_____

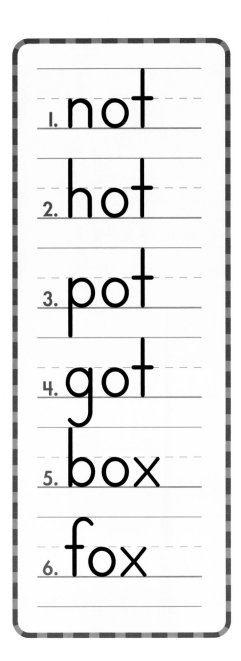

1. not

2. hot

3. pot

4. got

5. box

6. fox

Write a spelling word in each blank.

1. Ice is cold. Fire is _____.

2. A glass is like a cup. A pan is like a _____.

3. **Net** is close to **not**. **Get** is close to _____.

4. An owl is wise. A _____ is sly.

5. A hole lets sand out. A _____ keeps sand in.

6. **OK** means "yes." _____ means "no."

1. on
2. mom
3. job
4. hop
5. top
6. mop

A. Write the words that end with **op**.

1. _____

2. _____

3. _____

B. Write a spelling word to answer each question.

4. Which word is the same backward and forward?

5. Which word is **no** spelled backward?

6. Which word starts with **j**?

Name _____

1. up
2. us
3. bus
4. cut
5. but
6. nut

Write the spelling words that begin like the picture names.

cub

1. _____

numbers

2. _____

umbrella

3. _____

bubble

4. _____

5. _____

6. _____

School/Home
This unit teaches **short u**. Ask your child to name other words that start with **short u** as in **up**.

Short u 77

Spelling and Phonics

Use the clues to find each word. Write the words.

up
us
bus
cut
but
nut

These words have two sounds and start with the same letter.

1. _____

2. _____

These words have three sounds and start with the same letter.

3. _____

4. _____

These words end with the same two letters.

5. _____

6. _____

7. _____

Name _____

Spelling and Reading

Write the missing spelling words.

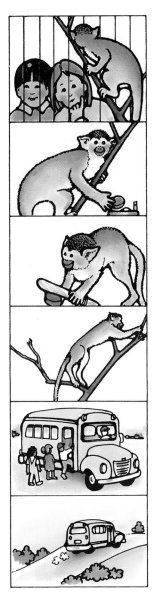

1. Gus looked at _____ .

2. Gus got a _____ .

3. Will Gus _____ the nut?

4. Then he went _____ a tree.

5. Now we have to get on the _____ .

6. We had fun, _____ we must go home.

up
us
bus
cut
but
nut

Short u 79

Spelling and Writing

Every person, animal, and plant needs care! Write about how you can show you care for people, animals, and plants.

More Words for Writing ▸ dug hum snug bump

Write the missing words.

1. Pip __?__ in the sand.

2. Dad hit a big __?__ .

3. Cal can __?__ in the tub.

4. I was __?__ in the bag.

Spelling and Thinking

1. fun
2. run
3. sun
4. tug
5. bug
6. rug

A. Write the spelling words that end in **ug**.

1. _____

2. _____

3. _____

B. Write the spelling words that end in **un**.

4. _____

5. _____

6. _____

 School/Home
This unit teaches **short u**. Ask your child to identify the rhyming words on the list.

Spelling and Phonics

Look at the pictures. Write the rhyming words to finish each sentence.

1. I have _____ playing in the _____ .

2. Jill had to _____ on the _____ .

3. Did you see the mother _____ give her child a <u>hug</u>?

4. Can that <u>bun</u> _____ ?

fun
run
sun
tug
bug
rug

Name _____

Spelling and Reading

Write the spelling word that matches each meaning.

1. This word means "a good time."

_____

_ _ _ _ _ _ _ _ _ _ _ _ _ _ _ _ _ _ _

_____

2. It is another name for an insect.

_____

_ _ _ _ _ _ _ _ _ _ _ _ _ _ _ _ _ _ _

_____

3. This is a covering for a floor.

_____

_ _ _ _ _ _ _ _ _ _ _ _ _ _ _ _ _ _ _

_____

4. You do this when you pull on something.

_____

_ _ _ _ _ _ _ _ _ _ _ _ _ _ _ _ _ _ _

_____

5. It gives us heat and light.

_____

_ _ _ _ _ _ _ _ _ _ _ _ _ _ _ _ _ _ _

_____

6. This means "to move very fast on foot."

_____

_ _ _ _ _ _ _ _ _ _ _ _ _ _ _ _ _ _ _

_____

fun
run
sun
tug
bug
rug

Spelling *and* Writing

A Summer Day

Write a story about a summer day.
Use as many spelling words as you can.

More Words for Writing ▶ **cub   bud   pup   hut**

Write a word to finish each sentence.

1. A small [house icon] house is a

   _____ .

2. A small [dog icon] dog is a

   _____ .

3. A small [flower icon] closed flower

   is a _____ .

4. A small [bear icon] bear is a

   _____ .

Spelling and Thinking

1. bad
2. yet
3. fix
4. dot
5. hug
6. tub

Name each picture. Match the sound you hear at the beginning, middle, and end of each picture name to write a spelling word.

1. _____

2. _____

3. _____

4. _____

5. _____

6. _____

bad
yet
fix
dot
hug
tub

Answer the questions.

1. Which word has **short a** in the middle?

_____

- - - - - - - - - -

_____

_____

2. Which word has **short o** in the middle?

_____

- - - - - - - - - -

_____

_____

3. Which word has **short e** in the middle?

_____

- - - - - - - - - -

_____

_____

4. Which word has **short i** in the middle?

_____

- - - - - - - - - -

_____

_____

5.–6. Which words have **short u** in the middle?

_____

- - - - - - - - - -

_____

_____

_____

- - - - - - - - - -

_____

Name _____

Spelling and Reading

Write the spelling word that fits each sentence.

1. Can I __?__ the net?

_____

_____

2. Is the __?__ red?

_____

_____

3. The cat was __?__ .

_____

_____

4. You can __?__ Mom.

_____

_____

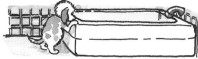

5. Can pup get in the __?__ ?

_____

_____

6. Can you see the sun __?__ ?

_____

_____

bad
yet
fix
dot
hug
tub

Spelling and Writing

How to Fix a Flat Tire

First get a tire pump. Take the cap off the valve [image] of the flat tire. Screw [image] on the tire pump. Pump until the tire is hard. Take the tire pump off. Screw the valve cap [image] on.

Have you ever fixed anything that was broken? How could you fix a torn picture? The broken leg of a doll? Write about something you have fixed.

More Words for Writing ▶ mix   wag   pop   bend

Write the word that matches each clue.

1. to move from side to side

2. to make a loud, bursting sound

3. to blend together

4. to make something curved

Spelling *and* **Thinking**

1. a
2. I
3. to
4. of
5. the
6. was
7. are

A. Write the two spelling words that have only one letter.

1. _____

2. _____

B. Write the spelling word that ends with the sound of letter **v**.

3. _____

C. Write spelling words to finish the puzzle.

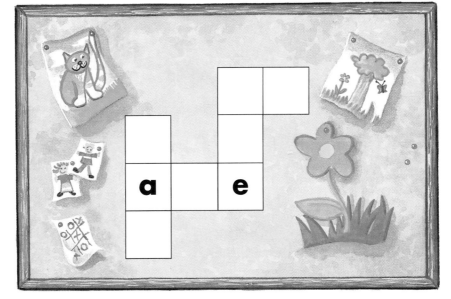

School/Home
This unit teaches commonly used writing words.
Help your child practice writing each word on the spelling list.

Words Writers Use 89

a
I
to
of
the
was
are

A. Use the clues to find the words. Write the words.

1. ● one letter ■ always a capital
   ▲ sounds like its name
   _____

2. ● three letters ■ two sounds
   ▲ the **e** makes no sound
   _____

3. ● three letters ■ two sounds
   ▲ the **e** does make a sound
   _____

4. ● three letters ■ three sounds
   ▲ starts like **win**
   _____

5. ● one letter ■ one sound ▲ sometimes sounds like its letter name
   _____

B. Write the word that rhymes with the others.

6. too, two _____

7. love, dove _____

Name _____

Spelling **and** Reading

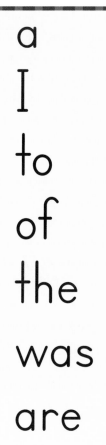

Write each word once to finish the sentences.

| a | the | of |

_____

1. Ed has one _____ these pens.

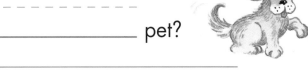

_____

2. Can Bess get _____ pet?

3. A cat was on _____ bed.

| I | to | was | are |

_____

4. The men _____ wet.

_____

5. _____ can help.

_____

6. Pam _____ on a jet.

_____

7. I ran _____ the bed.

Spelling and Writing

Write a story or poem about something or someone you would like to be. Have fun!

If I Were a Raindrop

If I were a raindrop,
I'd fall from the sky
And make a big puddle,
My friends and I,
And wait in the puddle
For someone like you
To fall in our puddle.
That's what I'd do!

Tom Lininger, Age 8

More Words for Writing ▶ **ago   easy   goes   only**

Complete the missing words.

A long time __1.__ there were no phones. It was not __2.__ to get a message to someone. Now you __3.__ have to dial or push a few buttons, and your voice __4.__ where you want it to!

1. a_____

2. e_____

3. o_____

4. g_____

Review Unit 11: Short u

Count and hop to find spelling words!

b c n p s t u

1. up
2. us
3. bus
4. cut
5. but
6. nut

➔ **7**
◄ **3**   1.

➔ **3**
➔ **4**
◄ **1**   3.

➔ **7**
◄ **2**   5.

➔ **1**
➔ **6**
◄ **2**   2.

➔ **2**
➔ **5**
◄ **1**   4.

➔ **1**
➔ **6**
◄ **1**   6.

School/Home
This unit reviews the **short u,** short vowels, and commonly used words.
Ask your child to read the spelling list on each page aloud.

1. fun
2. run
3. sun
4. tug
5. bug
6. rug

A. Write the words that end with **un** to finish the rhyme.

_____

1. Oh what _____

2. To jump and _____

3. In the summer _____ !

B. Write the words that end in **ug** to finish the rhyme.

_____

4. The _____ all snug

5. Inside a _____ will not like it

6. If you _____ !

1. bad
2. yet
3. fix
4. dot
5. hug
6. tub

Write the spelling word that begins with the same sound as each picture name.

1. _____

2. _____

3. _____

4. _____

5. _____

6. _____

Write spelling words to finish the story.

It ___1.___ a stormy night. The wind blew hard. ___2.___ could not sleep. I hid my head under my pillow. Mom came in ___3.___ room.

" ___4.___ you afraid?" she asked. "Would you like ___5.___ have ___6.___ glass ___7.___ milk?" she asked. I jumped out of the bed.

"Sure, Mom. I'll take care of you."

1. a
2. I
3. to
4. of
5. the
6. was
7. are

1. _____

2. _____

3. _____

4. _____

5. _____

6. _____

7. _____

Spelling and Thinking

Count and hop to find the words.

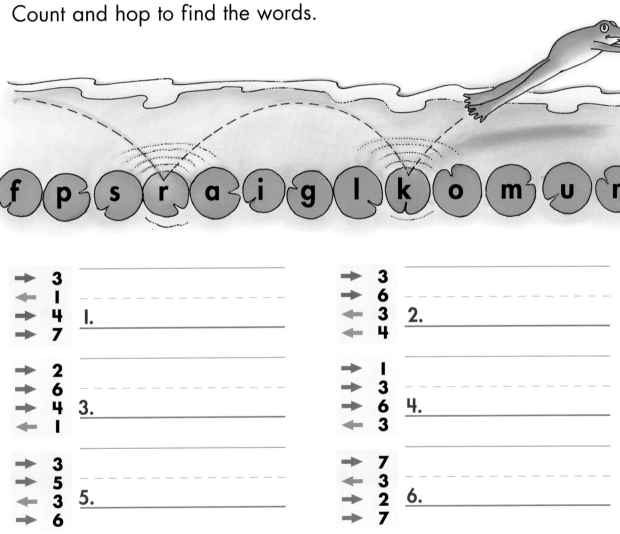

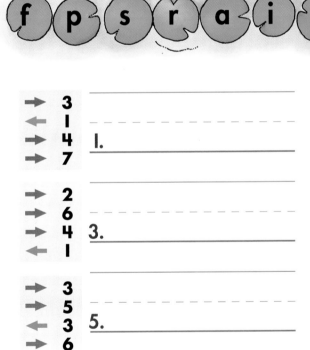

1. grin

2. spin

3. skip

4. frog

5. plum

6. slam

➡ 3
⬅ 1
➡ 4
➡ 7
1. _____

➡ 2
➡ 6
➡ 4
⬅ 1
3. _____

➡ 3
➡ 5
⬅ 3
➡ 6
5. _____

➡ 3
➡ 6
⬅ 3
⬅ 4
2. _____

➡ 1
➡ 3
➡ 6
⬅ 3
4. _____

➡ 7
⬅ 3
➡ 2
➡ 7
6. _____

School/Home
This unit teaches consonant clusters, such as **gr** in **grin**.
Help your child name other words that start with these clusters.

Spelling and Phonics

Write a rhyming word to answer each riddle.

1. Skinny smile: thin __?__

2. Hop over a hole: dip __?__

3. Fruity music: __?__ hum

4. Metal top: tin __?__

5. Hopper's run: __?__ jog

6. Make a jelly sandwich: jam __?__

grin
spin
skip
frog
plum
slam

Name _____

Write a spelling word to finish each sentence.

grin

spin

skip

frog

plum

slam

1. I can run and _ _ _ p.

_____

_ _ _ _ _ _ _ _ _ _ _ _ _

_____

2. A _ r _ _ got in the box.

_____

_____

_____

3. Dad had a big g _ _ _ !

_____

_ _ _ _ _ _ _ _ _ _ _ _ _

_____

4. I can _ _ i _ a top.

_____

_____

_____

5. Ron has a big p _ _ _ .

_____

_ _ _ _ _ _ _ _ _ _ _ _ _

_____

6. I will not _ _ a _ the door.

_____

_____

_____

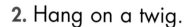

Spelling and Writing

Tell a caterpillar how to grow into a butterfly.

1. Make a cocoon.

2. Hang on a twig.

3. Fly away!

Put these pictures into words. Tell a tadpole how to grow into a frog.

More Words for Writing ▶ **grab   slip   snap   plug**

Complete each word to finish each sentence.

1. The dog will __?__ at the bug.

s _____

2. I can __?__ your hand.

g _____

3. Will the pig __?__ in the mud?

s _____

4. Let Mom __?__ in the lamp.

p _____

 **Initial Consonant Clusters**

Spelling and **Thinking**

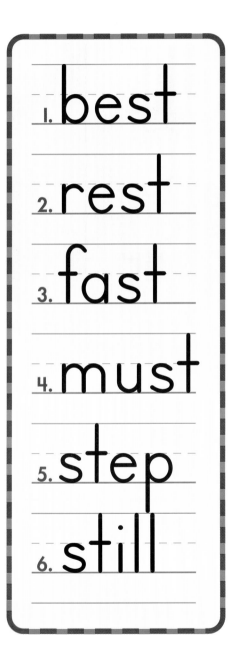

1. best

2. rest

3. fast

4. must

5. step

6. still

A. Write the spelling words that start with **st**.

1. _____

2. _____

B. Write the spelling words that end in **st**.

3. _____

4. _____

5. _____

6. _____

best
rest
fast
must
step
still

Write the rhyming word to finish each sentence.

1.–2. I did my _____ on the <u>test</u>.

Now I will _____ !

3. <u>Jill</u> is _____ on the <u>hill</u>.

4. Show some <u>pep</u>! Jump up the _____ !

5. It's a <u>blast</u> to ride this _____ !

6. We _____ <u>dust</u> off the <u>rust</u>.

Name _____

Spelling and Reading

Complete the spelling words to finish the story.

Jen is in a _____ race. Without taking one

__s_____ , she can __s_____ have

fun. Jen can go __f_____ !

Jen __m_____ not __r_____ until

the _____ race is over. The __b_____

racer will win a gold cup.

best
rest
fast
must
step
still

Spelling and Writing

Once, the Pony Express carried mail to the West. A horse and rider took mail bags many miles to where another horse and rider waited. The mail was carried from one part of the country to another.

Would this be a good way to send mail today? Why or why not? Write what you think.

More Words for Writing ▶ **post   stir   rust   stiff**

Write the missing words.

1.–2. He will _____ the paint with a _____ paddle.

3.–4. Ned will paint the _____ . It has _____ on it.

Name _____

Spelling and Thinking

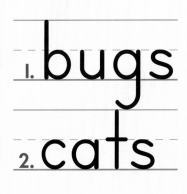

1. bugs
2. cats
3. pigs
4. sits
5. runs
6. gets

A. Add and write.

1. I  + I  = 2 _____ .

2. I  + I  = 2 _____ .

3. I ![pig] + I ![pig] = 2 _____ .

B. Look at the underlined word in each sentence.
Write a spelling word to complete the sentence.

4. Pat will <u>get</u> it. Pat _____ it.

5. Dad can <u>sit</u>. Dad _____ .

6. Mom can <u>run</u>. Mom _____ .

School/Home
This unit targets the **-s** ending. Ask your child to read the spelling list aloud.

Adding -s 105

Spelling and Phonics

Add **s** to each underlined word. Write the word the way it should be in the sentence.

bugs

cats

pigs

sits

runs

gets

1. The <u>pig</u> are in the pen.

_____

2. Sal <u>get</u> a big box.

_____

3. Bill <u>run</u> to the top.

_____

4. The red <u>bug</u> are on the steps.

_____

5. The frog <u>sit</u> on the log.

_____

6. Are the <u>cat</u> back yet?

_____

Name _____

Spelling and Reading

Look at the picture. Write the missing spelling words.

bugs
cats
pigs
sits
runs
gets

_____

A frog _____ on a log.

It _____ the _____ .

The _____ dig in the mud. The _____

rest in the sun. A lamb _____ in the grass.

Spelling and Writing

Toby likes to run. Before he runs, he puts on his running shoes and loose clothing. Then he does warm-up exercises.

Toby likes to run on grass. When he gets tired, he stops and walks. He runs again when he is ready.

What is your favorite sport? Do you know anyone else who does that sport? Talk to him or her about it. Write a newspaper article about the person.

More Words for Writing ➤ **cards chips pumps twins**

Write the missing words.

1. The two boys are ___?___ .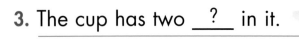

2. I got lots of ___?___ on my birthday.

3. The cup has two ___?___ in it.

4. Dad ___?___ gas into the car.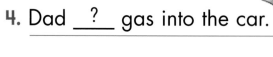

Spelling and Thinking

1. doing
2. going
3. seeing
4. feeding
5. feeling
6. keeping

Add **ing** to each word. Write the spelling word.

do	see	keep	feel	go	feed

1. _____

2. _____

3. _____

4. _____

5. _____

6. _____

School/Home
This unit focuses on the **-ing** ending. Help your child to say the spelling words with and without this ending.

Adding -ing   109

A. Write the words that have **long e** in the middle.
Circle the letters that spell this sound.

1. _____

2. _____

3. _____

4. _____

B. Add **ing** to each underlined word. Write the word as it should be in the question.

5. Where are you <u>go</u>? _____

6. What are you <u>do</u>? _____

7. Are you <u>feel</u> OK? _____

doing
going
seeing
feeding
feeling
keeping

Name _____

Spelling and Reading

Write a spelling word to complete each sentence.

doing
going
seeing
feeding
feeling
keeping

1. What is she _____ ?

2. She is _____ the horse's leg.

3. She is _____ if it is hurt.

4. She is _____ to fix it.

5. Matt is _____ the horse still.

6. He is _____ it grass.

Adding -ing   **111**

Spelling and Writing

Write a short poem. Use "A summer room" as the first line. What would you see from a summer room? You might also want to write a poem about a fall, winter, and spring room.

A Poem of Seeing and Feeling

A summer room
Where lying down
I see the clouds as they go past.

Yaha

More Words for Writing ► mowing   packing   bending   picking

Look at the picture. Write the best word.

1. __?__ down

2. __?__ plums

3. __?__ a bag

4. __?__ grass

Write the spelling word that names each picture.

1. grin

2. spin

3. skip

4. frog

5. plum

6. slam

1. _____

2. _____

3. _____

4. _____

5. _____

6. _____

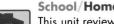

School/Home
This unit reviews consonant clusters and the word endings **-s** and **-ing**.
Ask your child to read the spelling list on each page aloud.

1. best
2. rest
3. fast
4. must
5. step
6. still

A. Write the spelling word that means almost the same.

1. nap

2. better than

3. quick

4. walk

B. Write the spelling word that rhymes with each word.

5. dust

6. hill

1. bugs
2. cats
3. pigs
4. sits
5. runs
6. gets

Write a spelling word to finish each sentence.

1. One <u>bug</u> _____ on a leaf.

2. Two _____ <u>sit</u> on the grass.

3. One <u>cat</u> _____ in the house.

4. Two _____ <u>run</u> in the sun.

5. One <u>pig</u> _____ lunch.

6. Two _____ <u>get</u> a mud bath.

1. doing
2. going
3. seeing
4. feeding
5. feeling
6. keeping

A. Write a spelling word to answer each problem.

1. feel + ing = _____

2. keep + ing = _____

3. go + ing = _____

4. do + ing = _____

B. Write the spelling word that goes with each picture.

5. _____   6. _____

Name _____

Spelling *and* Thinking

Find the spelling words. Circle them.

g	a	t	e	a	n
f	g	b	n	g	a
c	a	m	e	a	m
e	m	m	e	v	e
r	r	e	s	h	e	j
y	i	s	a	m	e

1. came
2. name
3. same
4. game
5. gate
6. gave

 School/Home
This unit targets the **long a** sound spelled **a-consonant-e**.
Ask your child to name rhyming words in the spelling list.

Spelling and Phonics

A. Write the spelling words that rhyme.

1. _____

2. _____

3. _____

4. _____

came

name

same

game

gate

gave

B. Count and hop to find the words.

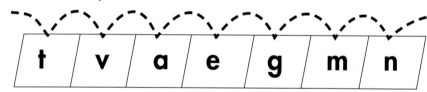

t	v	a	e	g	m	n

→ 5
← 2
← 1
→ 2
5. _____

→ 5
← 2
← 2
→ 3
6. _____

→ 5
← 2
→ 3
← 2
7. _____

→ 7
← 4
→ 3
← 2
8. _____

Name _____

Spelling and Reading

Write the missing spelling words.

Kate was at the __1.__ . Kate __2.__ in. Kate had a __3.__ .
The __4.__ of the game was Spin. I had the __5.__ game.
I __6.__ Kate a big plum.

came

name

same

game

gate

gave

1. _____

2. _____

3. _____

4. _____

5. _____

6. _____

Spelling and Writing

Mom and Dad wanted to name their first baby after Gramps. His name is Raymond. I was named Raylene. I like my name, especially when Mom calls me Ray. She says that I am a ray of sunshine!

You are a very special person. Your name was picked just for you! What is your name? Do you know why you were given that name? Do you have a nickname? Do you think that it is a good name for you? Write about it.

More Words for Writing ▶ **ape wake mane tame**

Write words to complete the sentences.

I had a  dream about a  lion and an  __1.__ . The  lion was __2.__. The ape was not. The ape pulled on the lion's  __3.__. The  lion made a loud noise. The noise made me __4.__ up.

1. ____________________

2. ____________________

3. ____________________

4. ____________________

Name _____

Spelling and Thinking

1. lake
2. rake
3. bake
4. make
5. take
6. made

A. Write the spelling word that goes with each group.

 pond    stream

1. _____

 fry    boil

2. _____

 shovel   hoe

3. _____

B. Write letters instead of numbers to make spelling words.

1 = a	
2 = d	
3 = e	
4 = k	
5 = m	
6 = t	

5 1 4 3   **4.** _____

5 1 2 3   **5.** _____

6 1 4 3   **6.** _____

School/Home
This unit targets the **long a** sound spelled **a-consonant-e**. Help your child read the spelling list aloud.

Spelling and Phonics

A. Circle the **long a** words. Then write them.

1. ran   take   man

2. rake   tack   map

3. rat   tap   made

1. _____

2. _____

3. _____

B. Circle the words below that rhyme. Then write them.

lake   fade   same

late   bake

gave   make

4. _____

5. _____

6. _____

lake
rake
bake
make
take
made

Name _____

Write the missing spelling words.

lake
rake
bake
make
take
made

Dad, Mom, and I will _____ camp at a

_____

_____. We will + _____ a big

_____

tent. Mom _____ a

_____

backpack for me. I will get sticks to _____ a fire.

Dad will b _____ the fish. Then I will

_____

_____ the leaves into a pile.

Spelling and Writing

Mom made this mobile for me. She knows that I like seashells. The tinkling sound makes me feel happy.

Have you ever made anything for someone?
Tell about what you made. Why did you make it?
How did you make it?

More Words for Writing ▶ **lace   lane   date   vase**

Write a word to name each picture.

1. _____

2. _____

3. _____

4. _____

Name _____

Spelling and Thinking

1. he
2. me
3. we
4. she
5. be
6. see

w   m   e   h   s   b

Match the shapes to the letters. Write the spelling words.

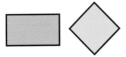

1. _____

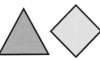

2. _____

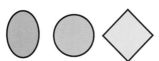

3. _____

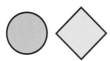

4. _____

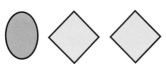

5. _____

6. _____

 School/Home
This unit targets the **long e** sound spelled **e** or **ee**. Ask your child to read the spelling list aloud.

Spelling and Phonics

A. Write the word that sounds like .

_____

1. _____

B. Write the **long e** word that tells about each picture.

_____

2. _____

3. _____

_____

4. _____

_____

5. _____

_____

6. _____

he
me
we
she
be
see

126 Long e

Name _____

Spelling and Reading

Write spelling words to finish the rhyme.

Instead of Ann, you can just say __1.__,
And Ben is sometimes known as __2.__.
A word for you and me is __3.__.
Together we're silly as can __4.__!
When my friends need help they ask __5.__.
We like each other, as you can __6.__.

he
me
we
she
be
see

1. _____

2. _____

3. _____

4. _____

5. _____

6. _____

Spelling and Writing

The Two of Us

I am me and you are you,
Together we add up to two.
Our color's different, so's our name,
But we can be friends just the same.

— Kevin O'Hara

Write about someone who is special to you. Why is he or she special? How do you show that a person is special?

More Words for Writing ▶ beet   peel   peek   deed

Write a word to finish each sentence.

1. Let me __?__ into the box.

2. Will you __?__ his orange?

3. I ate the big __?__ .

4. When you do something kind for someone, you do a good __?__ .

Spelling and Thinking

feel words:

1. feel
2. deep
3. keep
4. feed
5. seed
6. feet

Write the spelling words that end in **eep**.

1. _____

2. _____

Write the spelling words that end in **eed**.

3. _____

4. _____

Write the spelling word that ends in **l**.

5. _____

Write the spelling word that ends in **t**.

6. _____

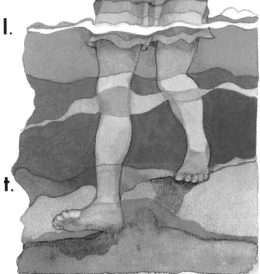

School/Home
This unit targets the **long e** sound spelled **ee**. Ask your child to circle **ee** in each spelling word.

Write the spelling word that rhymes with each picture.

feel
deep
keep
feed
seed
feet

1. _____

2. _____

3. _____

4. _____

5. _____

6. _____

Name _____

Spelling and Reading

Write the spelling words.

Do you want to grow a 🎃 pumpkin? Start with a 🎃 pumpkin __1.__ . Then put dirt in a __2.__ 🪴 tub. Is the dirt dry? 🪴 __3.__ it to find out. Seeds need 🪴 water, so __4.__ the dirt wet. You can __5.__ the seed with 🪴 plant food. Soon the seed will put down roots. The roots are like __6.__ . The plant will stand on them and grow strong. 🌱

feel
deep
keep
feed
seed
feet

1. _____

2. _____

3. _____

4. _____

5. _____

6. _____

Spelling and Writing

How does each of these children feel? Have you ever felt the same way? Write about what gives you these feelings.

More Words for Writing ▶ **weed   creek   sweep   cheek**

Write the word that fits each group.

1. dust, mop, __?__
_____

_____

2. nose, chin, __?__
_____

_____

3. river, stream, __?__
_____

_____

4. grass, flower, __?__
_____

_____

1. came
2. name
3. same
4. game
5. gate
6. gave

A. Fill in each blank to write a different spelling word.

1. __ __ t __ _____

2. __ __ v __ _____

B. Write the words that end with **ame**.

3. _____   4. _____

5. _____   6. _____

School/Home
This unit reviews **long a** and **long e**. Ask your child to read the spelling list on each page aloud.

Review 133

1. lake
2. rake
3. bake
4. make
5. take
6. made

Write the spelling words that begin with the missing letters.

a   **1.**   c   d   e   f   g   h

i   j   k   **2.**   **3.–4.**   n   o   p

q   **5.**   s   **6.**   u   v   w

x   y   z

1. _____

2. _____

3. _____

4. _____

5. _____

6. _____

he
1.

me
2.

we
3.

she
4.

be
5.

see
6.

Write the spelling word that stands for the underlined words.

1.
Lia and I looked out the window to see Ben. "Look," said Lia. "There's Ben. **2.** Ben must be going to the park." **3.** Lia called to Ben. "Hey! Will you take **4.** myself with you? I want to **5.** look at the new slide."

"Come on," said Ben. "We can all go."

6.
I called to my dad. "We'll stay at the park."

1. _____

2. _____

3. _____

4. _____

5. _____

6. _____

A. Follow the directions to write the spelling words.

1. Write the word that starts like and ends like **read**.

2. Change one letter to make SEEDS .

3. Change two letters to make a word that means **touch**.

4. Change one letter to make .

B. Write the words that rhyme with **beep**.

5. _____

6. _____

Spelling Words box:

1. feel
2. deep
3. keep
4. feed
5. seed
6. feet

Spelling and Thinking

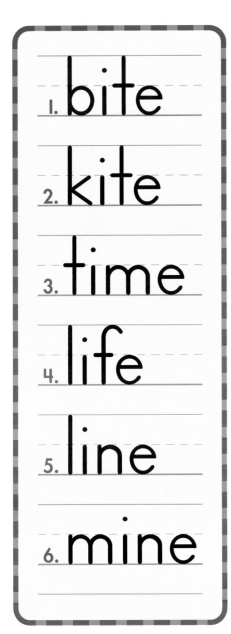

1. bite
2. kite
3. time
4. life
5. line
6. mine

A. Write a spelling word for each picture.

1. _____

2. _____

3. _____

B. Finish the crossword puzzle.

Across ➡
I. A clock shows the __?__.

Down ⬇
2. If it belongs to me, it is __?__.

Across ➡
3. A bird has __?__, but a stone does not.

School/Home
This unit targets the **long i** sound spelled **i-consonant-e**. Ask your child to name the spelling words that rhyme.

Long i   137

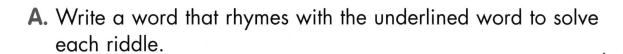

Spelling and Phonics

bite
kite
time
life
line
mine

A. Write a word that rhymes with the underlined word to solve each riddle.

_____

1. Tiny bug's nibble: <u>mite</u> _____

2. Paper cloud: <u>white</u> _____

3. Juice break: <u>lime</u> _____

4. Thin marking: <u>fine</u> _____

B. Write the word that rhymes with each picture.

5. _____

6. _____

Name _____

Spelling **and** Reading

Write a missing spelling word to finish each sentence.

1. Did he take a ____ of my sandwich?

2. It is ____ to go to bed.

3. I want to fly a ____.

4. Which box is ____?

5. I will draw a ____.

6. I had the best time of my ____.

bite
kite
time
life
line
mine

1. _____

2. _____

3. _____

4. _____

5. _____

6. _____

Spelling and Writing

Have you ever heard of Theodore Seuss Geisel? You may know him as Dr. Seuss. Dr. Seuss wrote children's books. As a young boy, Dr. Seuss enjoyed drawing and writing. He wrote his first book just for himself! He also drew cartoons for magazines and even made some movies.

Dr. Seuss did many things in his life. Other people have, too. Write about some things you would like to do.

More Words for Writing ▶ 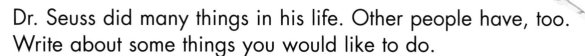 **tide   vine   pine   hive**

Write a word that rhymes with the word in ( ) to complete the sentences.

1. Did you sit under the __?__ tree? (**fine**)

2. The jellyfish came in with the __?__. (**ride**)

3. The busy bees are in the __?__. (**five**)

4. The deer like to eat this __?__. (**line**)

Spelling and Thinking

Long i

1.	bike
2.	like
3.	hike
4.	hide
5.	ride
6.	side

A. Write the spelling word that names each picture.

1. _____

2. _____

3. _____

4. _____

B. Circle the hidden spelling words. Write them.

_____

5. **l i s i d e q e d i**   _____

_____

6. **b i s d h i l i k e**   _____

School/Home
This unit targets the **long i** sound spelled **i-consonant-e**. Ask your child to read the spelling list aloud.

Spelling and Phonics

bike
like
hike
hide
ride
side

A. Write the words that rhyme with **tide**. Circle the letters that are the same.

1. _____

2. _____

3. _____

B. Put the letters together. Write the words.

4. h + ike = _____

5. b + ike = _____

6. l + ike = _____

Name _____

Spelling and Reading

bike
like
hike
hide
ride
side

Write the missing spelling words.

In the City

I __1.__ to live in the city.

I can __2.__ on a train.

I can __3.__ in the park.

I can __4.__ on the street.

I can lean on the __5.__ of the building and watch the people go by.

I can ride my __6.__ to the store.

1. _____

2. _____

3. _____

4. _____

5. _____

6. _____

Spelling *and* Writing

Me

I am six years old,
As happy as can be.
I can ride a bike.
I can read a book.
My name is Victor
And I like being me.

—Victor A. Wheeler

Change the poem so that it describes you. How old are you? What can you do? What is your name?

More Words for Writing ▶ **wide   rice   dive   wipe**

Write a word to complete each sentence.

1. **W**ise **W**illy opened the **w**indow __?__.

2. **R**ick's pet **r**at ate the __?__!

3. **D**o **d**ucks __?__ for their **d**inner?

4. **W**e **w**ill __?__ the **w**agon **w**ith **w**ax.

Name _____

Spelling and Thinking

1. no
2. go
3. so
4. hope
5. rope
6. home

Look at the shape around
each letter in the grid.
Write the spelling words.

m	o	p
s	h	g
n	r	e

1. _____

3. _____

5. _____

2. _____

4. _____

6. _____

School/Home
This unit targets the **long o** sound spelled **o** or **o-consonant-e**. Ask your child to circle the **o-consonant-e**
spelling pattern in the last three words on the list.

Use the clues to find each word. Write the words.

These rhyming words have two letters.

1. _____

2. _____   3. _____

This word rhymes with **dome**.

4. _____

The last three letters are the same in these words.

5. _____   6. _____

no

go

so

hope

rope

home

Name _____

Spelling and Reading

Write the missing spelling words to finish the letter.

Dear Tim,

My **1.** is in the desert. I **2.** to a little school. Sometimes there is **3.** rain for a long time. It is **4.** hot and dry. There are not many plants. I wove this **5.** for you. I **6.** you like it.

Love,

Maria

1. _____

2. _____

3. _____

4. _____

5. _____

6. _____

Spelling and Writing

People live in different kinds of homes. Some people live in houseboats. Some people live in mobile homes. Some people live in houses. Some people live in apartment buildings.

What kind of home do you live in? Write about your home. What do you like most about it?

More Words for Writing ▶ **cone   dome   hole   hose**

Write the missing words.

1. It lives in a ___?___ in the ground.

_____

_____

2. Did you get wet from the ___?___ ?

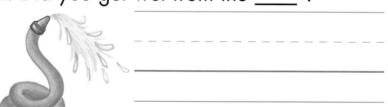

_____

_____

3. Look at the big ___?___ on that building!

_____

_____

4. I found this pine ___?___ under the tree.

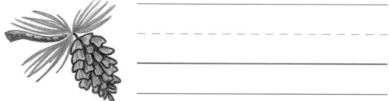

_____

_____

Name _____

Spelling and Thinking

Write a spelling word to name each picture.

1. nose
2. rose
3. bone
4. note
5. pole
6. rode

1.

2.

3.

4.

5.

6.

1. _____

2. _____

3. _____

4. _____

5. _____

6. _____

School/Home
This unit targets the **long o** sound spelled **o-consonant-e**.
Ask your child to circle the spelling words that rhyme.

Spelling and Phonics

nose
rose
bone
note
pole
rode

A. Write the words that rhyme with **hose**. Circle the letters that are the same.

_____   _____

1. _____   2. _____

_____   _____

B. Put the letters together. Write the words.

_____

3. n + ote = _____

4. p + ole = _____

5. b + one = _____

6. r + ode = _____

Name _____

Spelling and Reading

Write the silly sentences.

1. A bee __?__ on his __?__ .

2. A __?__ is on the __?__ .

3. A __?__ is on the __?__ .

| nose |
| rose |
| bone |
| note |
| pole |
| rode |

1. _____ .

2. _____ .

3. _____ .

People like roses because they smell sweet and come in many colors. If you give a rose to someone, it usually means that you love that person.

If you had a rose, who would you give it to? Why? Who would you like to get a rose from?

More Words for Writing ▶ **code   woke   mole   stove**

Write the missing words.

1. My cat __?__ me up.

2. The __?__ dug a hole.

3. We will make up a secret __?__ .

4. The pot is on the __?__ .

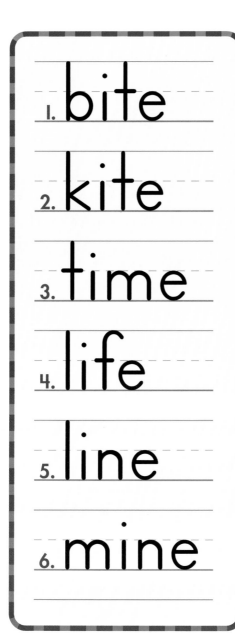

1. bite
2. kite
3. time
4. life
5. line
6. mine

A. Write the spelling word that goes with each picture.

1. _____

2. _____

3. _____

4. _____

B. Fill in the blanks to write spelling words.

5. _ _ f _ _____

6. m i _ e _____

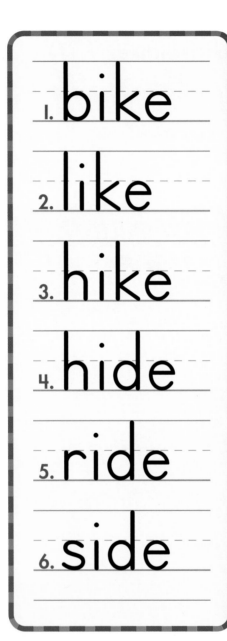

1. bike
2. like
3. hike
4. hide
5. ride
6. side

A. Write the words that end with **ide**.

1. _____

2. _____

3. _____

B. Write the words that end with **ike**.

4. _____

5. _____

6. _____

1. no
2. go
3. so
4. hope
5. rope
6. home

Circle the **long o** words. Write them.

1. hop
   hope
   _____

2. house
   home
   _____

3. rope
   romp
   _____

4. go
   got
   _____

5. so
   sock
   _____

6. not
   no
   _____

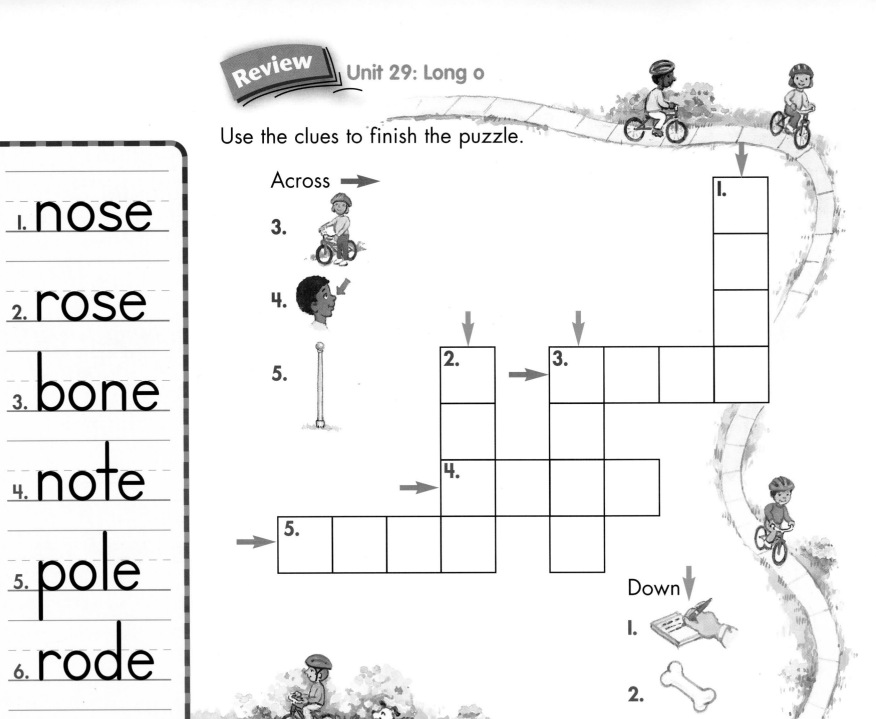

Use the clues to finish the puzzle.

Across

3.

4.

5.

1. nose
2. rose
3. bone
4. note
5. pole
6. rode

2.

3.

4.

5.

Down

1.

2.

3.

Name _____

Spelling and Thinking

Unit **31**

oo, yoo

1. do
2. you
3. zoo
4. use
5. room
6. soon

Write the spelling words that begin with the missing letters.

a b c   e f g h i

j k l m n o p q

t   v w x

1. _____ 2. _____

3. _____ 4. _____

5. _____ 6. _____

School/Home
This unit targets the oo and yoo sounds. Ask your child to use each spelling word in a sentence.

oo, yoo **157**

Spelling and Phonics

A. Write the spelling words with **oo**.

1. _____

2. _____

3. _____

B. Write the spelling word that sounds like **u**.

4. _____

C. Write the spelling word that begins with the letter **u**.

5. _____

D. Write the spelling word that has two letters and rhymes with **to**.

6. _____

do

you

zoo

use

room

soon

Name _____

Spelling **and** Reading

Write the missing spelling words.

1. What can we __?__ ?

2. We will make a __?__ .

3. We can __?__ this box for a pool.

4. It has __?__ for seals.

5. Can __?__ help me find the tape?

6. Our zoo will __?__ be finished.

do
you
zoo
use
room
soon

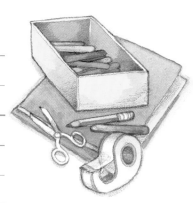

1. _____

2. _____

3. _____

4. _____

5. _____

6. _____

Spelling and Writing

Most big cities have zoos. A zoo is a place where people can see animals that they do not usually see. It takes the planning and work of many people to keep a zoo running smoothly.

What kind of work has to be done at a zoo? Would you like to work at a zoo? Why? What would you like to do? Write about it.

More Words for Writing ▶ moon   broom   spoon   stool

Complete the crossword puzzle.

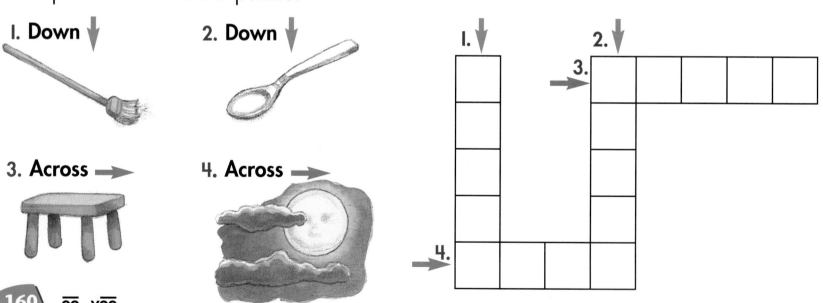

1. Down ⬇

2. Down ⬇

3. Across ➡

4. Across ➡

o͞o, yo͞o

Name _____

Spelling and Thinking

Write the spelling word that rhymes.

1. back

2. pack

3. neck

4. pick

5. sock

6. duck

1. crack, tack

_____

_____

2. clock, lock

_____

_____

3. speck, deck

_____

_____

4. track, sack

_____

_____

5. truck, buck

_____

_____

6. stick, tick

_____

_____

Write the word that rhymes with the underlined word to solve each riddle.

back
pack
neck
pick
sock
duck

1. Cargo van for quackers: _____ truck

2. Fast grab: quick _____

3. Painted foot: mock _____

4. Box of small nails: tack _____

5. Kiss from a parakeet: _____ peck

6. Carried behind: _____ pack

Name _____

Spelling and Reading

Write the missing spelling words.

Meg's Duck

Meg has a pet __1.__ . Its __2.__ is brown and

its __3.__ is black. Meg let me __4.__ it up. I fed

it a __5.__ of crackers. When I put it down, it pecked at

my __6.__ . I guess it thought I was a worm!

back
pack
neck
pick
sock
duck

1. _____

2. _____

3. _____

4. _____

5. _____

6. _____

Spelling and Writing

A duck is a bird. Ducks spend a lot of time in water, swimming and diving for food. Their bills are wide and flat to scoop up tiny animals and plants in the water. Their feathers are oily and fit tightly together. The feathers make a waterproof coat and help ducks stay on top of the water.

Why do you think ducks have webbed feet? Do any other animals have webbed feet? Why?

More Words for Writing ▷ **tuck quack crack cluck**

Write the words to finish the sentences.

Mother Hen and Mother Duck carefully __1.__ their eggs under them. They hear a loud __2.__ ! Mother Hen says, " __3.__ !" Mother Duck says, " __4.__ !" See what has happened!

1. _____

2. _____

3. _____

4. _____

Spelling and **Thinking**

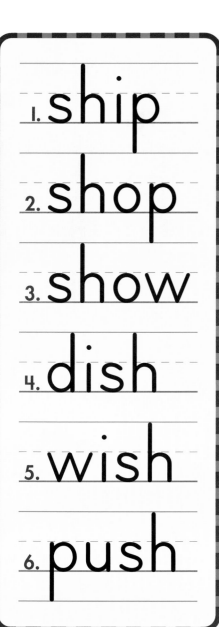

1. ship
2. shop
3. show
4. dish
5. wish
6. push

A. Write the word that goes with the meanings.

1. or "to look for things to buy"

_____

_____

2. or "to send"

_____

_____

3. or "to let someone see something"

_____

_____

4. or "to put food in a dish"

_____

_____

B. Circle the spelling words. Then write them.

5. "I wish I had help!"

_____

_____

6. "I will help you push."

_____

_____

School/Home
This unit targets the **sh** sound. Ask your child to circle **sh** in each spelling word.

sh 165

Spelling and Phonics

ship
shop
show
dish
wish
push

1.–2. Write the spelling words that rhyme with

_____

_____

3. Write the spelling word that rhymes with

_____

4. Write the spelling word that rhymes with

_____

5. Write the spelling word that means the opposite of **pull**.

_____

6. Write the spelling word with the **long o** sound.

_____

Name _____

Write the missing spelling words.

	ship
	shop
	show
	dish
	wish
	push

1. We are going on a  _____ .

2. Mom will 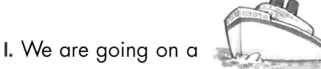 _____ me the rooms.

3. We can  _____ on the ship.

4. I want to get a  _____ for Spot.

5. I can _____ the elevator buttons.

6. I _____ I could steer the ship.

sh 167

Spelling and Writing

The Cat's Wish

I wish for grass to run in.
I wish for sun to sleep in.
I wish for mice to chase—
And a kind hand to pet my face.

How do you think a mouse would feel about
the cat's wish? What might the mouse wish for?
Write about it.

More Words for Writing ▶ shut crash hush shake

Write the word that goes with the action in the picture.

1. _____

2. _____

3. _____

4. _____

Name _____

1. that
2. then
3. this
4. bath
5. path
6. with

A. Add **h** to the end of each word.
Write the new word.

1. pat _____

2. bat _____

3. wit _____

B. Add **t** to the beginning of each word.
Write the new word.

4. hat _____

5. his _____

6. hen _____

School/Home
This unit targets the **th** sound. Ask your child to circle **th** in each of the spelling words.

th 169

Spelling and Phonics

that
then
this
bath
path
with

A. Write the words that rhyme. Circle the letters that are the same.

1. _____

2. _____

B. Write the words that begin with **th**.

3. _____

4. _____

5. _____

C. Write the words that end with **th**.

6. _____

7. _____

8. _____

Name _____

Spelling and Reading

Write the missing spelling words to finish the story.
One word will begin with an uppercase letter.

1. Jimmy will play __?__ me.

2. Will you hand me __?__ pot?

3. __?__ it will be your turn to cook.

4. We will take __?__ cake to Mom.

5. "Did you make that __?__ ?"

6. "It is time for your __?__ !"

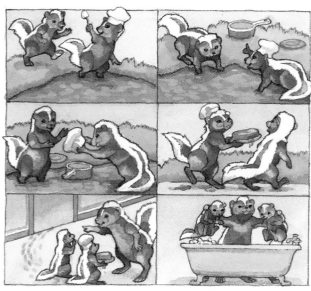

that
then
this
bath
path
with

1. _____

2. _____

3. _____

4. _____

5. _____

6. _____

Spelling and Writing

If you go to a forest, you can walk along paths and see many kinds of trees and flowers. If you are very quiet, you will see birds and other animals and where they live.

Follow the path. Write about what you see.

More Words for Writing ▶ **thin   thump   thud   booth**

Cross out the wrong word. Write the word that rhymes.

1. First we heard a <u>bump</u>!

_____

- - - - - - - - - - - - - - -

_____

_____

2. Then there was a loud <u>mud</u>!

_____

- - - - - - - - - - - - - - -

_____

_____

3. I saw a <u>tin</u> shadow on the wall!

_____

- - - - - - - - - - - - - - -

_____

4. This is a scary <u>tooth</u>!

_____

- - - - - - - - - - - - - - -

_____

1. do
2. you
3. zoo
4. use
5. room
6. soon

A. Write a spelling word to fill in each blank.

1. **Slow** is the opposite of **fast**.
   Late is the opposite of ____ .

2. A drawer is part of a desk.
   A ____ is part of a house.

3. Some people live in a town.
   Some animals live in a ____ .

B. Use the code to write spelling words.

| 1 = d | 2 = o | 3 = e | 4 = s | 5 = u | 6 = y |

4. 6 2 5 _____

5. 1 2 _____

6. 5 4 3 _____

School/Home
This unit reviews the o͞o and yo͞o sounds, **ck, sh,** and **th**. Ask your child to read the spelling list on each page aloud.

Review 173

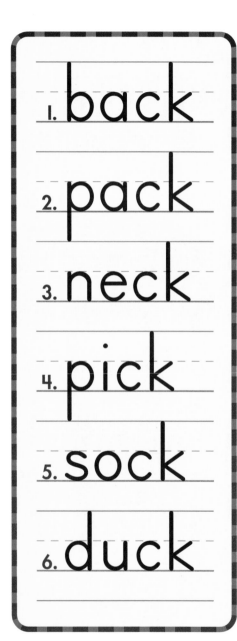

1. back
2. pack
3. neck
4. pick
5. sock
6. duck

Write the spelling word that goes with each picture.

1.

2.

3.

4.

5.

6.

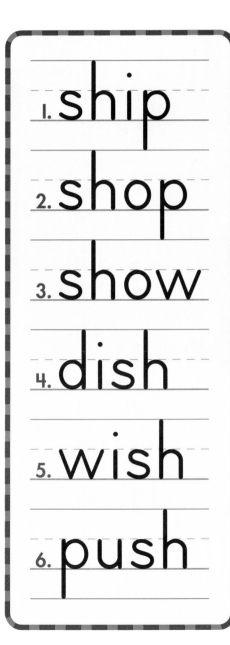

1. ship
2. shop
3. show
4. dish
5. wish
6. push

A. Write the words that end with **sh** like  .

1. ____________ 2. ____________

3. ____________

B. Write the words that start with **sh** like  .

4. ____________ 5. ____________

6. ____________

Look down and across. Circle the spelling words.

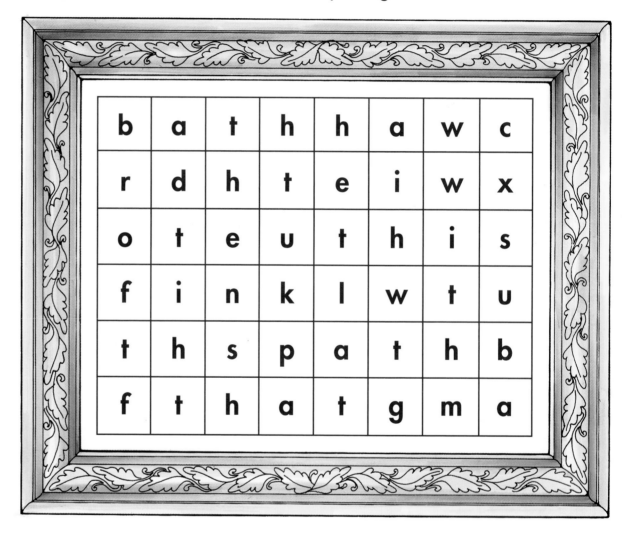

1. that
2. then
3. this
4. bath
5. path
6. with

b	a	t	h	h	a	w	c
r	d	h	t	e	i	w	x
o	t	e	u	t	h	i	s
f	i	n	k	l	w	t	u
t	h	s	p	a	t	h	b
f	t	h	a	t	g	m	a

Spelling Study Strategy

Look ➡ **Say** ➡ **Cover** ➡ **See** ➡ **Write** ➡ **Check**

1 **Look** at the word.

2 **Say** the letters. Think about how each sound is spelled.

3 **Cover** the word or close your eyes.

4 **See** the word in your mind. Spell the word to yourself.

5 **Write** the word.

6 **Check** your spelling.

A-B-C Order

Words in a dictionary are in a-b-c order. Words that start with **a** are first. Words that start with **b** are next. Words that start with **z** are last.

Fill in the blanks to write the **abc**'s in order.

a   b   _____   d   e   _____   g   _____   i   j

_____   _____   m   n   _____   p   q   r   s

_____   u   _____   w   _____   y   _____

Read the words below. Then copy them to show the order you would find them in a dictionary.

zoo	ant	duck
1.	2.	3.

Guide Words

There are two words at the top of each dictionary page. These words are called **guide words**.

The first guide word is the first word on that page.

The other guide word is the last word on that page.

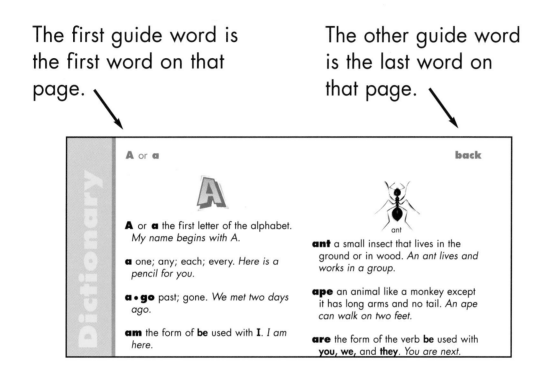

All the words on this page fall between the guide words in a-b-c order.

Circle the words that you would find on the dictionary page above.

ant   dog   milk   fall   are   back

Entries

Here is an entry from your **Spelling Dictionary**.

> **pet** an animal kept with people.
> *A cat may make a good pet.*

A dictionary **entry** is all the information about one word. An entry is the **entry word,** the **definition,** and the **sample sentence**.

1. The entry word is the word you are looking up.

Write the entry word here. _____

_____

2. The definition tells what the entry word means.

Circle the definition in the entry above.

3. The sample sentence uses the entry word. It helps you understand the word.

Underline the sample sentence in the entry above.

4. Circle the pair of guide words that could be on the page with **pet**.

　　　a • back　　　**soon • sweep**　　　**path • pop**

Here is an entry from your **Spelling Dictionary**.

> **frog** a small animal with webbed feet that lives
> near water. *A frog can jump far.*

An **entry word** is the word you are looking up. It is the first word in the entry. The entry word shows you how to spell the word. Entry words are in **bold type**.

1. Circle the entry word in the entry above.

The **definition** is the next part of an entry. The definition tells you what the entry word means.

2. Underline the definition in the entry above.

Here is another entry from your **Spelling Dictionary**.

> **note a.** a very short message or letter. *Let's write
> Mom a note.* **b.** a sign in music. *This is a quarter note.*

Sometimes an entry word can have more than one meaning. It will have more than one definition in the entry. Find two definitions for the word **note**.

3. Draw one line under the first definition.

4. Draw two lines under the second definition.

Sample Sentences

The **sample sentence** in a dictionary entry can be very helpful. The sample sentence uses the entry word in a sentence. The sentence can help you understand the entry word. It can help you know how to use the word. Sample sentences are in *italic type*.

1. Underline the sample sentence in this entry from your **Spelling Dictionary**.

> **moon** the body that shines in the night sky.
> *A full moon looks like a big circle.*

An entry also shows different **forms** of words. An entry will show the forms of action words. Forms are in **dark type**.

2. Underline the forms in the entry below.

> **hope** (hopes, hoped, hop·ing) to wish or expect.
> *I hope you will visit us soon.*

An entry will show the plurals of naming words. **Plural** means "more than one." Plurals are in **dark type**.

3. Underline the plural form in the entry below.

> **bus** (bus·es *pl.*) a long car or van that can carry many people. *We ride a bus to school.*

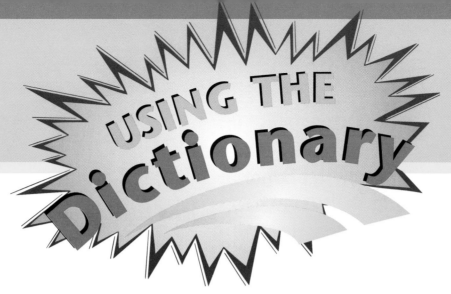
USING THE Dictionary

The **Spelling Dictionary** is the place to learn many helpful things about the spelling words.

The **entry** is the entry word, the definition, and the sample sentence.

The **entry word** is the spelling word you look up. Entry words are listed in a-b-c order.

The **definition** tells you what the word means.

ant

ant a small insect that lives in the ground or in wood. *An ant lives and works in a group.*

The **sample sentence** shows how the word is used in a sentence.

A or **a** the first letter of the alphabet. *My name begins with A.*

a one; any; each; every. *Here is a pencil for you.*

a • go past; gone. *We met two days ago.*

am the form of **be** used with **I**. *I am here.*

an one; any; each; every. We use **an** before words that begin with the vowel sounds of **a, e, i, o,** and **u**. *I ate an apple an hour ago.*

and a. with; together with; besides. *She likes to sing and dance.*
b. added to. *In math, 4 and 5 are 9.*

ant

ant a small insect that lives in the ground or in wood. *An ant lives and works in a group.*

ape an animal like a monkey except it has long arms and no tail. *An ape can walk on two feet.*

are the form of the verb **be** used with **you, we,** and **they**. *You are next. They are last.*

at in or by a place or thing. *Chang is at school.*

back the part of the body on the other side from the chest. *Give her a pat on the back.*

bad (worse, worst; bad•ly) not good, right, or healthy. *Eating too much is bad for you.*

bag

bag a sack; a container made of soft material. *Scott will take the bag with food in it.*

bake (bakes, baked, bak•ing) to cook in an oven. *We bake bread.*

bath a washing of the whole body. *We gave our dog a bath.*

be (am, are, is, was, were, been, be•ing) **a.** to equal. *Anna answered, "2 and 3 are 5."* **b.** to happen. *What time will the game be?*

bed

bed a thing to sleep or rest on. *Meg can make her bed.*

beet a plant grown for its juicy root. *He ate the red beet.*

bend (bends, bent, bend•ing) **a.** to make something curve. *Help me bend this wire.* **b.** to stoop or lean over. *Can you bend and touch your toes?*

best better than all others. *That was the best lunch I ever had.*

bib a cloth tied under a baby's chin to keep his or her clothing clean. *The baby's bib was full of food.*

big large. *Our school is big.*

bike

bike a bicycle. *Juan rides his bike.*

bit past tense of **bite**. *He bit into the apple.*

bite (**bites, bit, bit·ten** or **bit, bit·ing**) to grab, hold, or cut with the teeth. *When I lost my front teeth, it was hard to bite.*

bod • y (**bod·ies** *pl.*) all the parts that make up a person or an animal. *Take good care of your body.*

bone a hard part inside the body; a part of the skeleton. *Your longest bone is in your leg.*

booth a. a stand where something is sold. *Our class ran an art booth at the school fair.* **b.** a closed place. *Use the phone in that booth.*

box (**box·es** *pl.*) a case to hold things. *I have a toy box.*

broom

broom a brush with a long handle, used for sweeping. *You can use the broom to sweep the walk.*

bud the small beginning of a flower or leaf. *That bud will be a rose.*

bug an insect, usually one that crawls. *Even a small bug can crawl fast.*

bump a. to knock or hit against something. *Try not to bump into the wall.* **b.** a raised place. *The bump in the road makes the car bounce.*

bus

bus (**bus·es** *pl.*) a long car or van that can carry many people. *We ride a bus to school.*

but **a.** yet; however. *I will come, but I want to eat lunch first.* **b.** except. *We can go any day but Monday.*

came past tense of **come**. *They came to see us last week.*

can (**could**) **a.** to know how or to be able to. *He can play the piano.* **b.** a metal container. *Here is a can of peas.*

card a small piece of stiff paper. *We wrote each letter on a separate card.*

cat

cat **a.** a small furry animal that can purr. *Our cat loves to sit on my lap.* **b.** any larger animal that is also a part of the cat family. *A lion is a cat.*

cheek

cheek the side of the face below the eye. *She had a little smudge on her cheek.*

chip a small piece broken or cut off something. *Glue this chip back onto the cup.*

cluck a sound made by a chicken. *When a hen calls her chicks, it sounds like "cluck, cluck."*

Spelling Dictionary

cod a big fish often used for food. *Cod live in cold water.*

code a set of signals for sending messages. *Our club made up a secret code.*

come (comes, came, come, com·ing) **a.** to move closer. *Come over to my house.* **b.** to happen. *Our birthdays come once a year.*

cone **a.** an object that is round at one end and pointed at the other. *She made a cone of paper.* **b.** the seed pod of an evergreen tree. *That pine cone grew on a white pine tree.*

crack **a.** to break or split without snapping apart. *The glass may crack when I wash it.* **b.** to make a sudden snapping noise. *Did you hear the thunder crack?*

crash the very loud noise of something falling, breaking, or hitting. *The tree fell with a loud crash.*

creek a small stream. *The ducks swim in the creek.*

cub

cub a young bear, lion, or wolf. *We saw a bear cub at the zoo.*

cut (cuts, cut, cut·ting) to split with something sharp. *Let's cut this apple in half.*

dad a short word for **father**. *My dad took us for a walk.*

date the time when something happens. *July 4 is an important date.*

deed an act; a thing done. *Helping Jill clean her room was a good deed.*

deep going far down or back. *Big fish swim in deep water.*

den **a.** the home of a wild animal. *The lion cubs stay near their den.* **b.** a small room where one can read, relax, or work. *Mother is watching TV in the den.*

did past tense of **do**. *I did my homework last night.*

dig (**digs, dug, dig·ging**) to make a hole in the ground. *Dogs dig holes with their front paws.*

dish

dish (**dish·es** *pl.*) **a.** something that holds food. *Put the dish on the table.* **b.** to serve food. *Mom will dish out the green beans.*

dive (**dives, dived** or **dove, div·ing**) to jump headfirst into water. *Seals dive to catch fish.*

do (**does, did, done, do·ing**) to act, make, perform, or carry out. *Everyone in the class will do something different.*

dome a round roof or cover. *Dad put the cheese under a glass dome.*

dot **a.** a small round spot. *There was a dot of ink on my new shirt.* **b.** to mark with a small round spot. *Be sure to dot that i.*

duck

duck a swimming bird with webbed feet, a short neck, and a flat bill. *The duck swam in the pond.*

dug past tense of **dig**. *Dan dug a deep hole.*

eas•y not hard to get or do. *A toy on wheels is easy to pull.*

fast able to act or move quickly. *We can run fast.*

feed (feeds, fed, feed•ing) to give food to. *We must feed the horses.*

feel (feels, felt, feel•ing) **a.** to touch. *Feel the soft fur of the cat.* **b.** to have the feeling of being. *I feel cold.*

feel•ing a. what you feel in your mind; an emotion. *Birthdays bring a happy feeling.* **b.** a form of **feel**. *She is feeling better now.*

feet more than one foot. *Many animals have four feet.*

fix (fix•es, fixed, fix•ing) to repair or mend. *Grandpa can fix that broken toy.*

foot (feet *pl.*) the part of the body at the end of the leg. *I can stand on one foot.*

fox

fox (fox•es *pl.*) a wild animal like a dog but with a bushy tail. *The fox ran into the forest.*

frog

frog a small animal with webbed feet that lives near water. *A frog can jump far.*

fun a good time; happy play. *We had fun at the zoo.*

game a. a way to play that follows rules. *Let's have a game of tag.* **b.** the things needed to play a game. *Where is your game of checkers?*

gate

gate an opening like a door in a fence or wall. *She closed the garden gate.*

gave past tense of **give**. *We gave Mr. Russo a flower.*

get (**gets, got, got** or **got·ten, get·ting**) **a.** to come to have; to receive. *Our class will get new desks.* **b.** to bring. *I will get you a glass of milk.*

give (**gives, gave, giv·en, giv·ing**) to hand over; to let have. *I will give you this ball.*

go (**goes, went, gone, go·ing**) to move away to another place. *Let's go to your house to play.*

got past tense of **get**. *She got some carrots for a snack.*

grab (**grabs, grabbed, grab·bing**) to take hold of suddenly. *The boys grab their coats and run for the bus.*

grin (**grins, grinned, grin·ning**) to smile broadly. *The teacher may grin at my joke.*

had past tense of **have**. *We had fun at the park.*

has a form of **have**. *She has a sunny smile.*

Spelling Dictionary

hat a covering for the head; a cap. *My hat keeps my ears warm.*

have (**has, had, hav·ing**) to own; to possess. *I have a red cap.*

he that boy or man. *He is a good boy.*

hen

hen a female chicken or other bird. *Your hen can lay eggs.*

hide (**hides, hid, hid·den** or **hid, hid•ing**) to put or keep out of sight. *Let's hide the gifts quickly.*

hike a. a long walk. *We took a hike in the woods.* **b.** (**hikes, hiked, hik·ing**) to take a long walk. *Let's hike up that hill.*

him that boy or man. *Mike looked hungry, so I gave him an apple.*

his belonging to a boy or a man. *Ted likes to play with his dog.*

hive a box or other place where bees live. *Can you see any honey in the hive?*

hog a full-grown pig. *The hog eats lots of corn.*

hole an opening or empty space. *A nail makes a hole in the wall.*

home the place where a person lives. *My home is an apartment.*

hop (**hops, hopped, hop·ping**) to move by jumping lightly. *Rabbits hop quickly.*

hope (**hopes, hoped, hop·ing**) to wish or expect. *I hope you will visit us soon.*

hose a rubber or plastic tube that carries water. *Mom used the hose to water the garden.*

hot very warm; having a high temperature. *The stove is hot.*

hug

hug (hugs, hugged, hug·ging) to put the arms around something. *I hug my brother.*

hum (hums, hummed, hum·ming) to sing with the lips closed. *All day she liked to hum the new song.*

hush (hush·es, hushed, hush·ing) to make still or quiet. *See if you can hush the baby.*

hut

hut a little house or cabin that is plain and simple. *We camped in huts.*

I me; myself; the person talking. *I am learning to spell.*

if a. whether. *Do you know if Carmen is coming?* **b.** though. *Even if it rains, we'll still go.*

in a. inside. *We live in town.* **b.** during. *It rained in the morning.*

is a form of **be**. *Kevin is tall.*

it that thing. *It is my book.*

Spelling Dictionary

jet

jet a kind of plane with a strong engine. *The big jet took off with a loud roar.*

job the work that one does. *Taking out the trash is my job.*

jog (**jogs, jogged, jog·ging**) to run at a slow, steady pace. *Mrs. Morgan likes to jog every day to keep fit.*

jot (**jots, jot·ted, jot·ting**) to write something quickly. *Jot down this name on your list.*

keep (**keeps, kept, keep·ing**) **a.** to hold on to; to save. *Kim wants to keep all her old schoolwork.* **b.** to let stay; to have. *Todd can keep his socks in the top drawer.*

kite

kite a paper or cloth toy that can fly in the air on the end of a long string. *My kite is red.*

lace fine threads woven together in an open pattern. *Her dress was trimmed with white lace.*

Spelling Dictionary

lake

lake an inland body of water. *We saw a sailboat on the lake.*

lamp an object that gives light. *Turn on the lamp.*

lane a narrow path or road. *We walked down the lane.*

lap the top part of a person's legs when sitting down. *Dad held the baby on his lap.*

lead (leads, led, lead·ing) to show the way; to take. *Will you please lead the dog back home?*

leg

leg the part of the body used for standing and walking. *We put our pants on one leg at a time.*

let (lets, let, let·ting) to allow; to permit. *Please let me go to the park.*

lid

lid a top or cover. *He put the lid back on the pan.*

life being alive. *We study the life of plants.*

like a. the same as; similar to. *Marie is like a sister to me.* **b. (likes, liked, lik·ing)** to enjoy. *I like the new family next door.*

line a. a long thin mark. *Draw a line on the paper.* **b.** a row of persons or things. *We stood in a line.*

make (makes, made, mak•ing)
a. to put together; to build, form, or shape. *Dad can make a great pie.*
b. to cause. *Singing can make me feel happy.*

man (men *pl.*) an adult male person. *Mr. Green is a nice man.*

mane

mane the long hair that grows on the back of the neck of a lion or horse. *A lion's mane makes him look important.*

mat a piece of fabric or woven straw; a small rug. *Wipe your feet on the mat near the door.*

me I; myself; the person talking. *Eric will go with Ann and me.*

meet (meets, met, meet•ing) to come face to face with; to come together. *I'll meet you down at the corner.*

men more than one man. *We watched the men working.*

mend to repair; to fix. *Can you mend the hole in the roof?*

mess a dirty or sloppy state of things. *My room was a mess before I cleaned it.*

met past tense of **meet**. *We met the new girl.*

mine belonging to me. *This box is mine.*

mix (mix•es, mixed, mix•ing) to put different things together. *I will mix nuts and raisins to make a snack.*

mole a small animal with smooth fur and small eyes that lives underground. *A mole has long claws.*

mom a short word for **mother**. *My mom has a good job.*

moon

moon the body that shines in the night sky. *A full moon looks like a big circle.*

mop a. a long-handled tool used to clean floors. *This mop has a sponge on one end.* **b. (mops, mopped, mop·ping)** to wipe with a mop or cloth. *Please mop up the water.*

mow to cut the grass. *She wants to mow the lawn this morning.*

must to have to. *You must come home at six.*

name a. a word or words to call a person, place, or thing. *His name is Ryan.* **b. (names, named, nam·ing)** to give a name to; to call. *They will name the boy after his grandfather.*

neck the part of the body that joins the head to the shoulders. *A giraffe has a very long neck.*

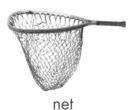
net

net a fabric with small holes. *He can catch a fish in his net.*

no a. the opposite of **yes**. *I voted "no" in a loud voice.* **b.** not any. *The dog had no food until we got home.*

Spelling Dictionary

197

Spelling Dictionary

nose the part of the face just above the mouth. *You smell with your nose.*

not a word that says **no**. *It is not a sunny day.*

note

note **a.** a very short message or letter. *Let's write Mom a note.* **b.** a sign in music. *That is a quarter note.*

nut a dry fruit or seed with a hard shell. *I ate one nut.*

of **a.** belonging to. *The roof of the house is brown.* **b.** made from. *The birds live in a nest of twigs.*

on **a.** above and held up by. *The lamp is on the table.* **b.** about. *I have a book on kites.* **c.** in use; not off. *She turned the radio on.*

on•ly **a.** single; by itself. *This is my only shirt with stripes.* **b.** no more than; just. *We have only one hour to get ready.*

ox

ox **(ox•en** *pl.*) a heavy bull used as a work animal. *The ox can pull a cart.*

pack to put carefully in a box or trunk. *Help me pack my suitcase.*

pan

pan a container used for cooking. *Use a small pan to heat the soup.*

pants a piece of clothing that covers each leg separately. *I wear pants.*

path a narrow trail or track. *The path leads up the hill.*

peek to take a quick look. *Close your eyes and don't peek.*

peel to take off the skin or outer layer. *We will peel the orange.*

pen a. a tool used for writing in ink. *My pen has blue ink.* **b.** a closed place to keep animals. *That pig lives in a pen.*

pet an animal kept with people. *A cat may make a good pet.*

pick a. to choose. *Which poem did you pick to read?* **b.** to pull off. *We can pick cherries from the tree.*

pig

pig a short animal with a thick body and a flat nose. *Our pig likes to dig.*

pin a. a thin piece of metal with a sharp point. *A pin can hold things together.* **b.** a small piece of jewelry with a sharp point. *Grandmother wore a pretty pin on her dress.*

pine an evergreen tree with leaves like needles. *We found a lot of cones under the tall pine.*

plug one end part of an electrical cord. *The lamp will go off if you pull the plug.*

plug in (plugs in, plugged in, plug·ging in) to connect to an electrical outlet. *Please plug in the iron.*

plum a small, soft, juicy fruit. *He picked a wild plum.*

pole a long thin piece of wood or metal. *We hung the flag from a pole.*

pop (pops, popped, pop•ping) to make a short, loud sound. *Did you hear the balloon pop?*

Spelling Dictionary

pot a deep, round dish or pan. *A pot is used for cooking.*

pump to fill by making something flow from one place to another. *Mom will pump the gas into our car.*

pup

pup a young dog; a puppy. *The happy pup wagged his tail.*

push (push·es, pushed, push·ing) **a.** to press on something to move it. *Push the gate shut.* **b.** to shove. *Try not to push the people in front of you.*

quack the sound made by a duck. *We heard the quack of the wild duck as it flew south.*

rake a. a garden tool with a long handle, used to gather leaves. *Put the rake in the shed.* **b. (rakes, raked, rak·ing)** to use this tool. *Will you help me rake the leaves?*

rest a. the other part; what is left over. *I ate ten nuts and Mark ate the rest.* **b.** to stop working; to relax. *Rest a minute before you go on.*

rice

rice a grain that people eat. *We ate chicken and rice.*

ride (rides, rode, rid·den, rid·ing) **a.** to sit on a moving animal or bicycle. *Can you ride a horse?* **b.** to go in a car, bus, or train. *How long does it take to ride to the city?*

Spelling Dictionary

rip (rips, ripped, rip·ping) to tear apart. *He may rip his pants on a nail.*

rod a long thin pole of wood, metal, or plastic. *Dad took his fishing rod to the pond.*

room a. a closed space inside a building. *Jan walked into the front room.* **b.** extra space. *Leave room on your paper for your name.*

rope a strong cord made by twisting smaller cords together. *We used a rope to hang the swing.*

rose

rose a flower that grows on a bush with thorns. *A rose smells sweet.*

rug a covering for a floor; a carpet. *He has a round rug in his room.*

run (runs, ran, run, run·ning) to move quickly; to go faster than walking. *Doug ran to first base.*

rust the coat of red-brown powder that forms on metals when they get damp. *My bike got a spot of rust when I left it outside.*

same just like another; identical. *Do it the same way I do.*

see (sees, saw, seen, see·ing) **a.** to look at; to use the eyes. *I can see a truck on the road.* **b.** to find out. *See if she needs any help.*

seed

seed the part of a plant from which another plant grows. *An acorn is the seed of an oak tree.*

Spelling Dictionary

set a. a group of things that belong together. *A carpenter needs a set of tools.* **b. (sets, set, set•ting)** to put in a certain place. *Set the dishes on the table.*

shake (shakes, shook, shak•en, shak•ing) to move quickly up and down or from side to side. *The label says "Shake well before using."*

she that girl or woman. *She likes to read.*

ship a. a large boat. *The ship sailed across the sea.* **b. (ships, shipped, ship•ping)** to send by boat, truck, or plane. *Our aunt will ship us a crate of apples.*

shopping

shop a. a small store. *We have a good hobby shop on our street.* **b. (shops, shopped, shop•ping)** to go to stores to buy things. *I'm going to shop for food.*

show (shows, showed, shown or showed, show•ing) a. to point out. *I will go first to show the way.* **b.** a movie, play, or TV program. *We saw a funny show.*

shut (shuts, shut, shut•ting) to close. *Will you shut the door, please?*

side a. a line that makes an edge. *Trace that side of the triangle.* **b.** the part between the top and the bottom or between the back and the front. *Use the door at the side of the house.*

sip (sips, sipped, sip•ping) to drink slowly, a little at a time. *I like to sip juice with a straw.*

sit

sit (sits, sat, sit•ting) to rest on the lower part of the body. *I will sit in this big chair.*

skip (skips, skipped, skip•ping) to move quickly by hopping twice on each foot. *The children want to skip around the yard.*

slam (slams, slammed, slam•ming) to shut hard with a loud noise. *The wind made the door slam.*

slip (slips, slipped, slip•ping) to slide suddenly. *Don't slip on the wet sidewalk.*

snap (snaps, snapped, snap•ping) **a.** to make a quick bite. *Look at that fish snap at the bait!* **b.** to break or crack. *I can snap this twig in two.*

snug cozy; comfortable. *Coats keep us snug and warm.*

so a. very. *I love you so much.* **b.** in the same way; also. *He is a good helper, and so is his sister.*

sock

sock a short stocking. *A long sock comes up to the knee.*

soon before long. *Dinner will be ready soon.*

spin (spins, spun, spin•ning) to turn around fast. *Can you see the wheel spin?*

spoon

spoon a tool for eating or serving that has a small bowl at one end. *Bring a spoon for the soup, please.*

step (steps, stepped, step•ping) **a.** a movement of the foot. *Simon says, "Take a big step."* **b.** a small platform for the foot. *I can stand on the top step.* **c.** to lift the foot and put it down in a new place; to walk. *Step to the front of the line.*

stiff not able to bend easily; hard. *My new toothbrush is stiff.*

still a. quiet; silent. *The house is very still at night.* **b.** even; yet. *Do you still have that old ball?*

stir (stirs, stirred, stir•ring) to move around or mix. *Jessica can stir the oatmeal with a spoon.*

stool

stool a seat with no back or arms. *Please push the stool under the table.*

stove

stove something you cook on. *The stove is hot.*

sun the star that gives us light and heat. *The sun sets in the west.*

sweep (sweeps, swept, sweep•ing) to clean by brushing away. *Sweep up this dirt with a broom.*

tag

tag a. a small piece of paper, metal, or plastic that contains information. *Can you read the price tag?* **b.** a game of chase. *Let's play freeze tag.*

take (takes, took, tak•en, tak•ing) a. to grip; to hold. *Take my hand when we cross the street.* **b.** to carry. *Can you take this box to the office?*

tame not wild; gentle. *You can pet the tame animals in the children's zoo.*

that (**those** *pl.*) the thing or person over there. *Greg sits at that desk by the window.*

the that one or those. *Did you find the pen or the pencils I lost?*

then a. at that time. *They came at 2:00, but I was gone then.* **b.** soon after. *We went to the movies, and then we came home.*

thin (**thin·ner, thin·nest**) not thick or fat. *A sheet of paper is thin.*

this (**these** *pl.*) the thing or person nearby. *Is this lunch box yours?*

thud a dull sound made when something big falls. *The suitcase fell with a thud.*

thump a loud bumping noise. *Did you hear that thump in the attic?*

tide the regular rise and fall of the water in the sea. *Let's look for seashells at low tide.*

time what a clock shows; the hour and minute. *What time is it?*

tip a. the end or point. *Can you touch the tip of your nose?* **b.** (**tips, tipped, tip·ping**) to lean; to push over. *The milk will spill if you tip the glass.*

to as far as; until; toward. *I'll walk to the corner with you.*

top a. the highest part. *A bird sat on the top of the tree.* **b.** a cover or lid. *Put the top on the jar, please.*

trot to move at a pace between a walk and a run. *A horse can trot or gallop.*

tub

tub a wide, open container for bathing or washing. *I took a hot bath in the tub.*

tuck to cover or wrap snugly. *I helped tuck the baby in the crib.*

tug (tugs, tugged, tug·ging) to pull hard. *My dog likes to tug on his leash.*

twin one of two persons born to the same mother at the same time. *Can you tell which twin is Don and which is Ron?*

up in, at, or to a higher place. *The rocket went up into the sky.*

us we; ourselves; the persons talking. *Play with us!*

use (us·es, used, us·ing) to put into action; to work with. *Jim will use a hammer to hit the nail.*

vase

vase a bottle or jar used to hold flowers. *Cindy put the roses in a pretty vase.*

vest

vest a short jacket with no sleeves. *My vest matches my pants.*

vine a plant with a long stem that can twist around things. *Grapes grow on a vine.*

wag

wag (wags, wagged, wag·ging) to move from side to side. *My dog likes to wag her tail as she eats.*

wake (wakes, woke or waked, waked or wo·ken, wak·ing) to stop or cause to stop sleeping. *Please wake me at six o'clock.*

was past tense of **is**. *He was sick.*

we us; ourselves; the persons speaking. *We are friends.*

weed a useless plant that grows wild. *Weeds grow fast.*

wet not dry. *The paint is still wet.*

wide (wid·er, wid·est) big from side to side. *A street with four lanes is wide.*

wig

wig a covering of false hair for the head. *I'm going to wear a wig.*

wipe (wipes, wiped, wip·ing) to clean or dry by rubbing. *Wipe the dust off the table.*

wish a. (wish·es, wished, wish·ing) to want; to hope for. *I wish you could come over.* **b.** something you want or hope for. *Did your wish come true?*

with a. in the company of. *They went with Uncle Charles.* **b.** using. *I washed my hands with soap and water.*

woke past tense of **wake**. *The thunder woke us up.*

yes the opposite of **no**. *Yes, you are right.*

yet a. up to now. *They haven't come yet.* **b.** still. *They may get here yet.*

you the person or persons spoken to. *You may go now.*

zip (zips, zipped, zip·ping) to close with a zipper. *Zip your jacket before you go out.*

zoo

zoo a place where live animals are kept for people to see. *In the zoo we saw some polar bears.*